Reading for Interest

Titles in order of difficulty

THE
BRAVE
AND
FREE

D. C. HEATH AND COMPANY

Boston

The stories and poems in this book were selected by

BARBARA NOLEN

and illustrated by

HARVE STEIN

Educational Consultants

PAUL WITTY *and* URSULA BRINGHURST

Reading for Interest

PAUL WITTY, *of Northwestern University, has served as consultant for this series, co-operating with the educators whose names appear beneath the titles listed below.*

Bigger and Bigger, by Inez Hogan. Illustrated by the author.
KATE KELLY, State Normal School, Castleton, Vermont

Little Lost Dog, by Lula Wright. Illustrated by Winifred Bromhall.
KATE KELLY, State Normal School, Castleton, Vermont

A Home for Sandy, by Romney Gay. Illustrated by the author.
LULA WRIGHT, Lincoln School, New York City

Rain and Shine, by Ardra Soule Wavle. Illustrated by Ruth Steed.
ETHEL MABIE FALK, Author and Lecturer, Madison, Wisconsin

Something Different, by Eva Knox Evans. Illustrated by Pelagie
Doane.
ETTA ROSE BAILEY, Matthew Maury School, Richmond, Virginia

Lost and Found, by Robin Palmer. Illustrated by Edna Potter.
RUTH BRISTOL, State Teachers College, Milwaukee, Wisconsin

Fun and Frolic, Barbara Nolen, Editor. Illustrated by Emma Brock.
FLORENCE BRUMBAUGH, Hunter College Elementary School, New
York City

Luck and Pluck, Barbara Nolen, Editor. Illustrated by Decie Merwin.
DOROTHY K. CADWALLADER, Carroll Robbins School, Trenton, New
Jersey

Merry Hearts and Bold, Barbara Nolen, Editor. Illustrated by Fritz
Kredel.
PHYLLIS FENNER, Public Schools, Manhasset, New York

The Brave and Free, Barbara Nolen, Editor. Illustrated by Harve
Stein.
URSULA BRINGHURST, New York University, New York City

CONTENTS

BAFFIN BAY TO PATAGONIA

DAYDREAMS

vi

With Skill and Pluck

Speed Ways

Working and Winning

Songs of Greatness

Cabins in the Clearing

Animals Brave and Wise

Hocus-Pocus

Indians and Pioneers

BAFFIN BAY TO PATAGONIA

TIVO AND HIS TURKEY

THURSDAY was always a great day in a certain little village high up in the mountains of Mexico, for Thursday was market day. Everybody for miles around arose very early on Thursdays, before the sun was up. They put on their best clothes and went down into the valley to sell things in the market-place, to hear about all the happenings of the week, and to buy things which were needed.

Young Tivo never went to the market, for he had nothing to sell, and he had no money with which to buy things. But on Thursdays he always got up as early as anyone else. He helped his mother cut great bunches of flowers to sell. When he had arranged them neatly for her in a basket, he helped his father pack the vegetables and sling the heavy hamper upon his back.

Tivo waved them good-by as they started down the steep path with their neighbors. He watched as the little procession zigzagged down the mountain — the men in their white pajamas, trotting beneath great bales and crates, the women loaded with gay flowers and fruit. Here and there he could see a small donkey with two huge packs, stepping along with the rest.

When the procession was out of sight, Tivo felt very lonely. He wished that he could be down there in the market-place with all the other villagers. If only he had a little money to spend, he would go down to the town and buy himself a fine hat, a red balloon, or a beautiful new blanket, a serape, to wear on holidays.

Tivo turned back to the house. He fed the pig and the cow and the chickens. After that, the day dragged until Tivo's mother and father came home tired and happy. They told him all about the things they had seen in the town, about the great cathedral with a tall golden altar and a beautiful Virgin with a jeweled crown, and about the brass band playing underneath the trees in the great square. They had bought a new kind of sandal made of old rubber tires with rubber knobs on the soles which would keep one from slipping on the mountains. There had been fireworks in honor of Saint Teresa's birthday.

Tivo listened eagerly. "Oh, Mother!" he cried. "I do so want to go to the market. Please let me go with you next time."

"You must wait until you have something to sell," replied his mother.

"Perhaps I could raise some vegetables all by myself," said Tivo. "Then I could go to the market."

"We have such a little bit of land for growing things," replied his mother. "Your father needs it all, and more."

Tivo's face fell.

"But," his mother said, "if you want something to sell in the market, just keep your wits working and you'll be sure to think of something."

She was right. On the very next day, just as the family was sitting down to dinner, in came the old mother turkey. She was leading a downy baby turkey.

4

"Is this the only baby you have hatched?" cried Tivo's mother angrily when she saw the one little turkey. "Then don't bring him to me! You can just take him right away and raise him all by yourself!"

"But, Wife," objected Tivo's father, "if you leave the baby turkey to his mother, she will surely take him into the woods, and the fox will eat him. Turkey mothers are so foolish."

"I cannot help it," replied Tivo's mother. "Baby turkeys are a great trouble to raise. You have to hunt them up and take them in when it rains. You have to keep them warm when it is cold. You have to feed them. For a whole brood of turkeys I would take the trouble, but for only one turkey, no!"

"Oh, Mother, let me have the little turkey," spoke up

Tivo. "I will gladly feed him and take care of him. I do not mind."

"You may have him and welcome," she replied.

"Oh, thank you, Mother!" cried Tivo. "And when he is grown, may I take him down to the town and sell him in the market-place?"

"Indeed, you may," promised his mother, "and you shall have the money to spend as you like. But I warn you, little turkeys are very hard to raise."

But Tivo was not easily discouraged. He got down on his knees beside the downy baby. "Come, Peepelo, little turkey," he called gently, and he spread corn meal upon the floor for the baby's dinner.

The little turkey looked at it for a moment with one beady black eye. He pecked at it curiously, and then he began eating in earnest. Peck-peck-peck went the tiny bill, and it was not long before the corn meal was all gone and Peepelo's crop stuck out like a ball.

Never was a little turkey better cared for than Peepelo. When Tivo had his breakfast in the morning, he took Peepelo upon his knee and fed him beans and little bits of tortilla from his own plate. At the first sign of a cloud in the sky, Tivo ran to find his baby. He kept him in the house until the last drop of rain had fallen.

Peepelo grew round and plump and friendly. He seemed like one of the family. At mealtime he came stepping into the kitchen, peeping loudly for his dinner. At night, warmly wrapped in a piece of an old blanket, he slept on the foot of Tivo's bed.

Peepelo kept on growing. After a few weeks his legs became long, and he began to shed the soft down which covered him. Then, a few weeks later, his new feathers began to appear. How handsome he looked! He was a fine half-grown turkey now and he began to feel the urge, as all turkeys do, to wander away and see the world. At last, one day, he wandered along the edge of the dark forest that lay beyond the maize fields. Tivo came running after him.

"Don't you dare go into the woods, you foolish little turkey!" cried Tivo. "Foxes are in there, and mountain lions, and wildcats. They all love the taste of a nice fat turkey and they will catch you and eat you up!"

But Peepelo was very curious. No sooner was Tivo's back turned than he hopped off again into the underbrush. It was dim and quiet in the woods. The rays of sun slanted through the foliage and made great patches of sunlight upon the ground. Peepelo ran from bush to bush, pecking off the worms and beetles. Deeper and deeper into the forest he went. It grew late. No more sunlight fell through the branches. But Peepelo did not notice. He was too busy.

Suddenly he caught sight of two gleaming eyes staring at him from the underbrush. Something told Peepelo that this meant danger. He huddled into the shadow of a rock, but it was too late. A tawny animal slunk out of the bushes and crept toward him. At first Peepelo was too frightened to move. Then he gave a screech and ran as fast as his awkward legs would carry him.

The fox came swiftly behind. Peepelo, glancing backward, could see his red tongue, his shining eyes. The fox lunged forward. His strong jaws closed upon Peepelo's tail feathers.

Then far away through the trees, he heard someone calling, "Peepelo! Peepelo! Where are you, Peepelo?" It was Tivo, coming to find him. Peepelo gave a loud peep of joy. He pulled with all his might. His tail feathers came out in the animal's mouth, and away went Peepelo. The fox was at his heels, but Peepelo had new life. He sped along toward the friendly voice.

Tivo saw the little turkey fleeing for his life and ran toward him. He snatched up his pet and went crashing through the bushes for home. The disappointed fox stole away into the bushes.

"You see! What did I tell you?" cried Tivo. "In a moment the fox would have eaten you!"

Peepelo nestled down in Tivo's arms and made happy little sounds in his throat. He made up his mind never to go into the woods again.

He never did. In the mornings when Tivo was helping his father in the maize fields, Peepelo remained safely at home with the chickens and the pig and the cow. He scratched contentedly for worms and watched for Tivo to come home. At noontime when Tivo came in from the fields, Peepelo ran to meet him. Tivo always lifted him, stroked his feathers, took him into the house, and gave the little turkey a part of his own dinner.

MARKET DAY

Peepelo was growing to be a handsome young turkey now. His tail had grown out again. The feathers around his neck shone like bronze. A fine black tassel hung smartly from his chest. He learned how to spread his tail into a beautiful fan and parade proudly before the chickens and the animals in the yard.

"Look, Tivo," said his mother one day. "See how your turkey struts! He is fully grown now. If you wish to take him to the market, now is the time. He is young and plump and tender."

Tivo thought of all the beautiful things to be bought in the market-place.

"Oh, Mother," he cried, "may I go with you next Thursday? I will take Peepelo and sell him in the market-place!"

"Yes, indeed, you may," replied his mother. "There is no use to put it off until your turkey is old and tough. No one would want him then."

On the very next Thursday, when the whole sky was pink with the sunrise, Tivo and his turkey joined the little procession that went trooping down the mountain.

Peepelo nestled warm and comfortable underneath Tivo's ragged serape. Only his head stuck out so that he might get a sight of the country as they passed along.

Down from the high mountain they wound, down from the brisk mountain air, the dark fir trees, and the tall pine trees, down into the warm country where palm trees waved and purple flowers climbed over the houses. Tivo had never seen so many or such beautiful houses — pale pink ones, cream-colored ones with blue borders around the doors and windows, others deep blue like the mountains, all with neat red-tile roofs. Tivo walked slower and slower, looking at all the strange new sights.

"Come, come, Tivo, keep up!" urged his mother. "We shall soon reach the hotel. You can stop in and try to sell your turkey. They always pay good prices."

Tivo ran forward and walked beside his parents, but he was very quiet.

"See, here is the hotel gate," said his mother, stopping in front of a great iron grill. "Just walk right through the patio and into the kitchen."

Tivo stood hesitating.

"What are you waiting for? Are you afraid?" asked his father.

As Tivo started slowly through the gate, his mother called, "Remember! Ask five pesos for your turkey. If they bargain with you, you can come down to three pesos. That is a very good price. Even two pesos would not be bad. But try to get three."

"I'll try to get three," promised Tivo, and the iron gate closed behind him. He looked at Peepelo resting on his arm. How his feathers glistened! What sparkling brown eyes he had! Tivo walked slowly into the kitchen.

The hotel keeper came bustling forward. He lifted Peepelo and held him up by the feet. He pinched him to see how firm he was. Poor Peepelo was not used to such treatment. He squawked indignantly.

"How much do you want for this turkey?" asked the hotel keeper.

"I'll take five pesos," replied Tivo. He looked curiously around the kitchen. There, hanging from a beam, were five other turkeys, stiff and cold.

"Five pesos!" exclaimed the hotel keeper. "I'll give you two."

"No, I can't let you have my turkey for that," replied Tivo.

"All right then, three pesos," said the hotel keeper. "Is it a bargain?"

"No, no," said Tivo with his eyes on those turkeys, "not for three pesos!"

"Then I'll give you four," said the hotel keeper grudgingly, "but it's an outrageous price."

Tivo looked down. Peepelo was busily pecking at one

of the buttons on his shirt front. "No, I can't take four pesos," he said hesitatingly.

"You must be crazy!" cried the hotel keeper. "Get along with you!"

Tivo hurried from the hotel.

"What is the matter?" asked his mother. "Wouldn't he give you your price?"

"I — I'd rather sell my turkey in the market," stammered Tivo.

On they started again, and at last they came to the market-place. Tivo's mother and father began unpacking their vegetables. They spread them in neat little piles upon broad banana leaves laid upon the sidewalk.

"You must walk around, Tivo," said his mother, "and see if you can sell your turkey."

Down the street went Tivo with his turkey. What fine things he saw in the stalls as he passed along! Sandals in this one, serapes in that one, hats in another one. Tivo stopped for a moment and looked at the hats. There was a beautiful one with a pointed crown and a leather band cut into the shape of horses' heads. Tivo tried it on. How fine he felt with the broad white brim curling up all around! The stall keeper looked at him admiringly. Peepelo gobbled as if he too were proud!

"How much is this hat?" Tivo asked.

"Only two pesos, and I might let it go for one and a half," whispered the stall keeper.

"Perhaps I shall buy this one in a little while," said Tivo, "as soon as I sell my turkey."

He walked slowly on, with Peepelo nestling on his arm, until he came to an old lady stooping over a charcoal burner. She was busy stirring something in a big bowl, but she looked up as Tivo went by.

"A fine turkey you have, my lad. What will you take for it?" she said.

Tivo stood miserably clasping Peepelo in his arms. He thought of the sandals, the hats. But they gave him no joy.

"I — I don't think I shall sell him right now," he stammered. He turned and ran back down the street.

"What is the matter?" asked his mother. "Didn't the old lady you talked to want to buy a turkey?"

"I — I think I can find a better place to sell him," said Tivo.

"Perhaps you are right," agreed his mother. "The butcher might give you a better price. His shop is in the great square opposite the cathedral."

Tivo walked slowly through the streets until he came to the square. Yes, there was the butcher shop, across the way from the great cathedral that pointed its towers into the sky.

The band was playing gaily in the square. In the churchyard were spread out other beautiful things for sale. Tivo gazed longingly at a leather belt, studded with brass. He fingered a beautiful serape. But he did not try it on. Instead he turned his back on the square.

When Tivo found his mother and father, they were busy packing up to go home.

"What!" cried his mother when she saw Tivo standing with Peepelo under his arm. "Weren't you able to sell your turkey to the butcher?"

Tivo hung his head.

"It's too bad," said his mother, "for we must be getting along now. There's no time to peddle him elsewhere. I'm afraid you'll have to take him back home again."

Tivo did not seem to mind. He hugged Peepelo close underneath his ragged serape. He settled his old hat upon his head and walked briskly along beside his mother and father.

That night Tivo lay upon his mattress of bamboo stalks and gazed happily at Peepelo roosting upon the foot of his bed. He thought of all the fine things he had seen in the town.

"But there was not anything that I liked half so much as my own Peepelo!" said he to himself.

Ellis Credle

BATTLE WITH A GIANT SQUID

BILLY was a fisherman's son living on Ruddy Cove, a fishing harbor on the bleak northeast coast of Newfoundland. All Newfoundland boys have adventures, and it was not surprising that Billy Topsail had one, too.

One gray evening late in September, Billy Topsail and Bobby Lot were returning from Birds' Nest Islands in Bobby's punt. The boys had gone out to hunt a group of seals, reported to have taken up a temporary residence there. They had a mighty, muzzle-loading, flint-lock gun. They were so delighted with the noise it made that they had exhausted their scanty supply of powder and lead long before the seals were in sight.

They had taken the shortest way home. It lay past Chain Hole, a small, deep bay with a narrow entrance, which was shallow at low tide. The entrance opened into a broad bay, and this narrow water passage was called a tickle — Chain Tickle.

"What's that in the tickle?" Billy exclaimed, as they were rowing past.

It was a black object, apparently floating quietly on the surface of the water. The boys gazed at it for a long time, but could make nothing of it. They were completely puzzled.

" 'Tis a small bit of wreck, I'm thinking," said Bobby. "Let's row close and see."

"Maybe 'tis a capsized punt."

When they were within about thirty yards of the object, they lay on their oars. For some reason they did not care to venture nearer. Twilight was then fast approaching. The light was already beginning to fail.

" 'Tis a wonderful queer thing!" Billy muttered, his curiosity getting the better of him. "Row ahead, Bobby. We'll go alongside."

"There's something moving on it," Bobby whispered, as he let his oars fall in the water. "Look! There's two queer, big, round spots on it — big as plates."

Billy thought he saw the whole object move. He watched it closely. It did stir! It was some living thing, then. But what? A whale?

A long, snakelike arm was lifted out of the water. It swayed this way and that, darted here and there, and fell back with a splash. The moving spots, now plainly gigantic eyes, glittered.

" 'Tis the devil-fish!" screamed Bobby.

Another arm was lifted up, then a third and a fourth and a fifth. The monster began to lash the water — faster and yet more furiously — until the tickle was heaving and frothy.

"Pull! Pull!" cried Bobby.

Billy, too, was in a panic. The boys turned the head of the punt and pulled with all their might. The water swirled in the wake of the boat. When they saw that the squid made no effort to follow, they got the better of their fright. Then they lay on their oars to watch the monster.

They wondered why it still lay in the tickle, and why

it so furiously lashed the water with its arms and great tail. It was Bobby who solved the mystery.

" 'Tis aground," said he.

That was evidently the situation. The squid had been caught in the shallow tickle when the tide, which ran swiftly at that point, was on the ebb. The boys took courage. Their curiosity made them bolder still. Once more they turned the punt about and pulled cautiously toward the tickle.

The daylight was almost gone, but there was still enough light to show the horrid eyes and writhing arms of the squid when the boat was yet a safe distance away. One by one the arms fell back into the water, as if from exhaustion. Then the tail beat more slowly. After a time all sound and motion ceased. The boys waited for some further sign of life, but none came. The squid was still, as if dead.

"Sure, he's dead now," said Billy. "Let's pull close."

"Oh, no, boy! He's but making believe."

But Billy thought otherwise. "I want that squid," he said in a dogged way, "and I'm going to have him. I'll sell him and get a new punt."

Bobby protested in vain. Nothing would content Billy Topsail but the possession of the big squid's body. Bobby pointed out that if the long, powerful arms were once laid on the boat there would be no escape. He recalled to Billy the story of the horrible death of Zachariah North, who, as report said, had been pursued, captured, and pulled under water by a devil-fish in Gander Bay.

It was all to no purpose, however, for Billy obstinately declared that he would make sure of the squid before the tide turned. He admitted a slight risk, but he wanted a new punt, and was willing to risk something to get it.

He proposed to put Bobby ashore and to approach the squid alone, but Bobby would not listen. Two pairs of hands might be needed in the boat. What if the squid were alive, after all? What if it laid hold of the punt? In that event, two pairs of hands would surely be useful.

"I'll go," he said. "But we must pull slow. And if we see so much as a wink of his eye we'll pull away."

They rowed nearer, with great caution. Billy moved to the bow of the boat. It was he who had the ax. Bobby, seated amidships, faced the bow. It was he who now did the rowing.

The squid was quiet. There was not a sign of life about it. Billy estimated the length of its body, from the beak to the point of the tail, as twenty feet, and the circumference as the size of a hogshead. Its arms, he thought, must be at least thirty-five feet long. When the boat came within that distance he shuddered.

"Are you sure he's dead?" Bobby whispered, weakly.

"I don't know," Billy answered, in a gasp. "I think so."

Bobby dropped the oars and stepped to the bow of the punt. The boat lost way and came to a stop within twenty feet of the squid. Still there was no sign of life.

The boys stared at the great, still body, lying quiet in the gathering dusk. Neither seemed to feel the slight trembling of the boat that might have warned them. Not a word was spoken until Billy, in a whisper, directed Bobby to pull the boat a few feet nearer.

"But we're moving already," he added, in a puzzled way.

The boat was very slowly approaching the squid. The motion was hardly noticeable, but it was real.

" 'Tis queer!" said Bobby.

He turned to take up the oars. What he saw lying over the port gunwale of the boat made him gasp, grip Billy's wrist, and utter a scream of terror.

"We're caught!"

The squid had fastened one of its tentacles to the punt. Another tentacle was poised above the stern, ready to drop and fix its suckers. The onward movement of the punt was explained.

Billy knew the danger, but he was not too terrified to act. He was about to spring to the stern to strike off the tentacle that already lay over the gunwale, but as he looked down to choose his step he saw that another of the ten powerful arms was slowly creeping over the starboard bow.

Billy lifted his ax and struck at that arm with all his might. The arm, injured, was withdrawn. Billy leaped to the stern, conscious in passing that still another arm was creeping from the water. He severed the tentacle on the port gunwale with one blow. When he turned to strike the one at the stern, it had disappeared. So, too, had the third arm. The boat seemed to be free, but it was still within grasp.

In the meantime the squid had awakened to furious activity. It was lashing the water with arms and tail, angrily snapping its great beak and throwing out streams of black water, making a black froth.

In this way, the creature showed its fear and distress. Had it not been aground, it would have backed swiftly into the deep water of the basin. But, finding itself at bay, it lifted one of its uninjured tentacles high above the boat. Billy made ready to strike.

By this time Bobby had mastered his terror. While Billy stood with uplifted ax, his eyes fixed on the waving tentacle overhead, Bobby pulled mightily on the oars. The boat slowly drew away from danger. In a moment the tentacle was withdrawn a short distance. Then like a flash it shot toward the boat, writhing as it came.

Billy struck blindly — and struck nothing. The tentacle had fallen short. The boat was out of danger!

But still Billy Topsail was determined to have the body of the squid. In spite of Bobby's protests, he would not abandon his purpose. He was only more determined than before. Bobby would not hear of again approaching nearer the squid, nor did Billy think it wise. But it occurred to Bobby that they might land and approach the squid from behind. If they could draw near enough, he said, they could cast the grapnel on the squid's back, and anchor it to a tree on shore.

"Sure," he said excitedly, "you can pick up a squid from behind, and it can't touch you with its arms! It won't be able to see us, and it won't be able to reach us."

So they landed. Billy carried the grapnel, which was attached to twelve fathoms of line. It had six claws with which to take a firm hold.

A low cliff at the edge of the tickle favored the plan. The squid lay below, and some twenty feet out from the rocky shore. It was merely a question whether Billy was strong enough to throw the grapnel so far. They tied the end of the line to a stout shrub. Billy cast the grapnel, and it was a strong, true cast. The iron fell fair on the squid's back. It was a capture.

"That means a new punt for me," said Billy, quietly. "The tide'll not carry that devil-fish away."

"And now," Bobby begged, "let's make haste home, for 'tis growing wonderful dark — and — and there might be another squid somewhere."

Norman Duncan

CATCHING A CONDOR

SNOW lay deep on the rugged slopes of Altar, one of the highest mountains of Ecuador. Dave Archer stood in the doorway of the farmer's hut where he was staying while his father carried on an engineering job. He watched the jagged crest of the mountain tear the wind-whipped clouds to shreds.

"It must be cold up there," he said to the farmer, who had come out to see what it was the American boy was looking at.

"Cold and still!" Señor Perez answered. "There is no sound whatsoever, except when the winds blow fiercely. That mountaintop is no place for any living thing — except, of course, the condors."

"The condors!" Dave echoed. "I'd forgotten about them. The biggest things that fly!"

"There is one, now," said Señor Perez, stepping into the open and pointing a bony finger toward the heavens.

Dave looked up into the sky. Presently he located a floating speck, far above.

23

"There are three condors that nest in the rocks near the peak," the farmer added. Even as he spoke, the giant bird glided smoothly toward the earth. A thousand feet above the high plateau it swung gracefully skyward again. The boy watched it, fascinated.

"I'd like to catch one," he said. "I'd like to take it back to New York when I go, and show my friends who keep canaries what a real bird is like."

"Catching a condor is easy," said the farmer. "We build a ring of stakes, and in the middle lay the carcass of an animal. The condors come down and eat all they can hold. Then we can lasso them easily, for in order to fly away they must first run along the ground, and there is no room to do that inside the stakes."

"Let's catch one, Señor Perez," cried Dave eagerly, "and surprise my father when he gets back from Quito."

"Alas," murmured Perez, "we have no wood for stakes here where there are no trees."

Above them the condor circled lazily in the sky.

Dave was disappointed. "There must be some way!" he said.

"Oh, yes," the man answered, "there is a way. But it is hard — and dangerous. You have to climb to the shoulder of the mountain where they live. I have done it many times, but never when the snow up there is deep."

Dave's eyes sparkled with a sudden excitement. He turned to the farmer, and laid hold of his arm. "Let's do it!" he urged.

Perez smiled at his eagerness. "Very well," he said with

a shrug. "Your father is my good friend. I will help you catch a condor. But we must start in the morning at dawn!"

That night Dave scarcely slept. Before the rising sun had tinted the snow on the peaks he was getting into his clothes.

"Put on all the clothes you have," Perez ordered. "Above the snow line, the wind cuts like ice."

When Dave walked outside the hut, the stars were fading and the sky was gray.

Perez shouted to him, "Come into the kitchen. My wife has some hot potato soup for you, and some bread and coffee."

At the side of the house Segundo, the farmer's son, and the hired man were loading a mule. "We have some meat for bait," Perez explained.

After Dave had gulped down the soup and the hot, black coffee, the party of four set off. Perez led the way up the steep mountain trail, with Dave close behind, followed by the peon. Last of all came the boy, Segundo, leading the mule.

From a distance the mountainside had looked fairly smooth. Now Dave discovered that there were grassy humps at the base, and that in many places the ground was steep and slippery. The others, with their rope-soled sandals, had no trouble at all, but Dave's feet slipped and he soon began to tire.

Presently they came to a belt of brushwood. Perez called a halt while he took from the mule's pack two sharp knives with heavy blades. One of these machetes he gave to Dave.

For a few minutes Dave enjoyed using his machete. Perez seemed tireless as he hacked at branches and thorns. Dave tried to keep pace with him, but it was no use. After half an hour Dave felt so tired that he could hardly stand. His right hand was bleeding, and he could no longer hold the machete. He was glad when Perez called a halt.

"We must not stop long," said the farmer, throwing himself down to rest. "Otherwise you will feel unable to go on."

When they started off again, Dave found his knees were still trembling. In a little while he could hardly lift his feet, and his breath came in gasps, but, ashamed to let the others know how he felt, he kept on. Just when it seemed as if all his endurance was gone, they stepped out of the bush onto the bare mountainside.

"Here we can rest," said Perez. "We will make camp

in this hollow, and Segundo can wait here with the mule and the food."

Quickly the two men cut branches and made a shelter. The boy built a fire in a rocky crevice, and prepared to make coffee. Dave wrapped himself in a blanket and lay down. He was too tired to think or move.

A little while later, they had a lunch of bread and coffee. Sitting up, Dave looked down the mountain. Thirteen thousand feet below, he could see the distant valley. The rivers looked like tangled silver threads. To the north, the mighty crest of Chimborazo appeared above a layer of clouds, with its snow-covered crater sparkling like a diamond collar in the morning sun.

Soon it was time to go on again. Perez handed Dave a sharp, iron-pointed pole. "Walk carefully," he said. "The ground is frozen between here and the snow line. There is a drop of two thousand feet, so take care not to slip."

Dave struggled to his feet, and they started up the slope. The peon walked behind, the pack on his back suspended in a kind of sling from a strap around his forehead.

Perez handed Dave a piece of string. "Better tie your hat on," he said. "The wind is getting strong."

Walking diagonally across the face of the mountain, they moved little by little up the steep slope and into the field of snow.

"Be careful!" shouted Perez over his shoulder. "The snow is deep in places."

Even as he spoke, one of his legs sank into the snow up to the knee and he fell on his face. A few moments later Dave's leg went in deep. As he fell, the pole flew from his grasp and went rolling down the slope. Perez threw out a hand to catch the boy before he, too, rolled down and over the cliff. Struggling to get up, Dave knocked Perez over backwards, and for an instant both were in grave danger of going over. But Perez clung to the boy, and jabbed his pole deep in the snow.

Dave realized then, with horror, how close he had come to ending both their lives, and he lay suddenly still. "I'm sorry," he said to Perez. "I guess I lost my head."

"It is nothing," Perez answered with a shrug. "We had better rest and eat some chocolate. We have another two thousand feet to go."

As they sat on a rock eating the food, the peon gave a loud hiss, and pointed upward. Above them, a condor came sailing out of the sky like a meteor. To Dave it seemed as big as an airplane.

"There's a beauty!" he said. "I'd like to catch him."

Perez chuckled. "That is an old one," he answered. "It would be too bad for you if you got a lasso around his legs and forgot to let go."

"I was wondering about that," said Dave. "Could a condor carry anyone away?"

"Not with its claws," Perez answered. "Their feet are not strong enough to lift anything so heavy."

Dave finished the last of his chocolate and stood up. "I'm frozen," he said, swinging his arms. "Let's get going!"

A few hundred feet from the top of the slope the ground was broken by rocks jutting out over deep snow. After several attempts to scramble over these, Perez called a halt.

"The snow is loose," he said. "It would be dangerous to go farther. We will find a flat rock to set the trap on and try it here."

A hundred yards away they found what they were seeking — a high, flat rock amid a cluster of other rocks behind which they could hide. From a net the peon took the bait — the animal killed the day before. He fastened a stout cord around its neck and hind legs, and lashed it to the rock. Over its body he laid the noose of the trap rope, leading the rope under the lashing cord and bringing the end down to their hiding place.

"Now," explained Perez, "when the condor feels the noose tighten around its ankles, it will let go of the bait and leap into the air to fly away. But the lashing cord will hold the trap rope down for us, and we shall not be dragged off the mountain."

These preparations completed, they crouched behind the leaning rock to await the coming of the bird. The minutes dragged by, and nothing happened. Dave thought he had never been so cold and miserable in his life. Then he began to feel violent cramps in his legs and he could not keep still. Perez made him lean against the rock, and rubbed his legs with snow. When the pain was gone, the three of them crouched close together against the rock, numb with cold.

Half an hour and then an hour went by. Dave could stand no more.

"Let's go!" he said desperately. "I'm freezing to death. No condor is worth this!"

Then the peon nudged him. Dave peered around the edge of the rock, and in an instant the cold was forgotten. On the crest of the mountain, far above them, perched a condor. The bird cocked his head, first this way, then that. Apparently satisfied that he was alone, he fixed his gaze on the food below. Dave sighed with disappointment as the great bird, instead of making for the bait, shot up into the air, flapping his wings. But Perez held up a warning finger. With a feeling of keen disappointment, Dave watched the condor going higher and higher in great circles till it was but a dot in the blue.

Suddenly Perez grew tense. "Here he comes!" he snapped, holding the rope at arm's length. Dave and the peon crouched against the rock, holding the free end of the rope. Over an angle of the rock, Dave saw the condor hurtle down out of the sky like a plummet. Surely it would be smashed to pieces against the mountain!

Then out shot the great wings to their full span. Down stretched the claws, fastening instantly on the carcass. Perez's arm jerked back, and the loop was over the feet of the bird.

"Grab it!" Perez yelled.

Dave and the peon threw their weight on the line. With mighty sweeps of his pinions, the big bird jerked at the rope. The air was filled with powdered snow, as the condor fought furiously to free itself.

Half blinded by the snow, Perez crept, foot by foot, toward the desperate creature.

The peon gave a sudden cry. "Look out! The cord is slipping!"

Though he could see little from where he stood, Dave could feel that something was wrong, for the bird was now bounding several feet in the air at every downward thrash of its wings.

"Quick!" yelled Perez. "Down! Pull down!"

He flung himself forward to catch the rope around the rock. Dave leaped to help him, and one of the giant wings struck him full across the face. With a cry, he fell backward, clinging wildly to the rope. The peon leaped over him, the loose end of the rope gathered in a loop.

"Lasso its head!" screamed Perez, hanging on grimly to the jerking line.

Dave pulled himself to his feet in time to see the condor slashing down at the peon with its sharp beak. As the head came down in a lightning stroke, the peon's arm flashed upward, and the rope snapped over the condor's neck.

Held fast by feet and neck, the bird stood quiet for an instant, as if accepting defeat. Dave, thinking the battle won, took hold of the neck rope, to help the peon tighten it. Like a flash the bird came to life again, flapping its wings in fury. Dave was jerked off his feet and bounced against the rock. When he got up, blood was trickling down his cheek.

"Wait!" said Perez, giving Dave the other rope to hold. "He will not be quiet till we cover up his eyes." With that, he took from the peon's pack a stout canvas bag about a foot in diameter. "Now pull down the head," he commanded.

That was easier said than done, for the bird was strong. Passing the rope around an angle of the rock, Dave and the peon pulled down the proud head of the condor till it could barely move. Then, with a lightning movement, Perez flung the bag over the bird's head, and the battle was won. With the bird's legs tied and its head in a canvas bag, it was easy for Perez to tie a wide strip of canvas around the sturdy body and wings so that the condor was helpless.

All that remained to be done was to get it down the mountain. With the heavy bird strapped to his back, Perez slid and slipped down the slope to the waiting mule. Dave marveled at the man's strength and skill.

When at last they reached the farm on the mountain-side, Perez chained the condor to a wagon beneath a shed at the edge of the potato patch, and gave him a barrel to perch upon.

"We will keep the chain short for a while," he said. "As the bird becomes tame, we can lengthen it so that he can move about."

For several days David could not get the captive to eat,

although he offered him the farmer's best guinea pigs and chickens. The condor would merely lash out with his beak, then go back to sulking. But it seemed to Dave that each time the attack was less and less savage.

Then one morning, quite suddenly, the bird flapped down from his barrel and pounced on the breakfast the boy had brought him.

Perez looked on, smiling. "Tomorrow," he said, "we can loose him a little, and in a few days, after we have trimmed a few feathers, you can carry him about on your arm."

It was two weeks, however, before Dave could lead his new pet about as he wished. As the bird flapped onto his barrel perch, now set out in the open, Dave called Perez to watch.

"He's so quiet and contented," said the boy, "I can't believe he was such a trouble to catch."

"You don't really know how near we came to losing him," Perez chuckled. "I suppose I can tell you now. When he knocked you over, I let go of the rope too. If the bird hadn't been more surprised than we were, he could have flown off with the rope and the bait as well."

Dave stared at him, amazed. "I'm glad I didn't know," he said. "I had the rope twisted round my wrist. He would have carried me off, too. I shouldn't have had a chance!"

Henry Lionel Williams

QUARRY GIRL

FROM the top of Mount Ararat, Mary could look
over city streets to the farms and the woods beyond, or
northeast to Boston bay with its islands. Mary had come
to the mountain before she could remember, to live with
her grandfather and grandmother in the one small house
on its top. Her grandfather was watchman for the quarries and lived in the little red house among the lilacs.

Mount Ararat was as wild as though the wilderness

still surrounded it. Its granite crest had been broken into quarry after quarry, most of them deserted now. The springs in the rock had filled these deserted quarries with pools of green water, very deep and dark. The water was no longer pumped out of the old quarry pits. They were given back to nature, with their sheer cliffs, their curious square corners, and their rusty derricks standing out against the sky.

Two or three of the quarries were still in operation. Here, during the daytime, gangs of men were at work. The donkey engines creaked and the derricks jerked slowly upward, bearing to the surface great blocks of granite split from the core of the mountain where they had lain since the earth was young.

The men who worked in the quarries spoke to Mary when they saw her and tried to offer her cookies from their lunch boxes, but she was shy with them. She wandered among the deserted quarries, among the sumacs and stunted willows above the cliffs.

On hot summer days, when the boys came up from the city below to swim in the pools of the old quarries, Mary would watch them wistfully from a distance. Sometimes the girls came too, calling and laughing. If anyone spoke to her she would blush and turn away her head and pretend that she had an errand to do. She did not know what to say to them. They all seemed so self-assured and easy with one another. Only she was an outsider.

"Oh, don't bother with her! It's only the quarry girl.

She's wild as a hawk," a boy shouted once when she had run away. The name stuck. Soon the other children from the city below called her the "quarry girl," and talked about her as they might have talked about some interesting wild creature.

A big pine tree with a double trunk grew at the very edge of the mountaintop overlooking the bay. Often Mary came there to sit and look down on the roofs and streets and the great blue bay beyond. Sometimes she took her sewing under the pine. Her grandmother always had plenty of hemming and darning for her to do.

One spring day when Mary came to the pine tree she noticed a new burrow among its twisted roots, quite a large burrow, she thought, with the fresh earth in front of it like a kind of veranda. When she told her grandfather about it he thought it must be a woodchuck's hole.

"Though I don't know where a woodchuck would come from, unless it had wings," he added.

Ararat had many birds, but Mary had never seen an animal large enough to make the burrow. She went back to the pine tree the next good day but still saw nothing. She tried to tell her grandfather about the strange odor she noticed around the burrow.

"That seems more like a fox than a woodchuck," said her grandfather, "but dear knows how a fox would get here, either."

"A wild animal will do anything which needs to be done," said her grandmother, overhearing the talk. "But if it's a fox, it will soon be after Mr. Kennedy's chickens

37

and then he'll not rest day or night till the poor thing's dead."

Halfway down the mountainside there were several houses and one or two stonecutters' sheds where the granite was chipped and shaped into blocks or headstones. Mr. Kennedy, who was a retired quarryman, lived there. He was the only man for miles around who still kept chickens.

After several rainy days, Mary picked her way through the puddles to her favorite pine tree again. She still saw nothing of the maker of the burrow, but she did find some feathers and a chicken-leg at the entrance. These she carefully gathered and threw over the cliff.

"If Mr. Kennedy saw this rubbish, he'd know just where to find you," she warned the dweller in the burrow. "You must be more careful."

Somehow, the unseen animal seemed to belong to Mary, to be in her charge, as though it had come to live under her protection. But Mary never saw it.

One dawn there was the sudden sound of a shot which re-echoed from the quarry walls until Ararat seemed ringing with shots. That day one of the stone-workers stopped at the little red cottage. He told how Mr. Kennedy had shot a fox robbing his chicken-yard.

Mary, who had come to the door, gave her grandfather a quick pleading look. If she had been afraid that he would speak of the pine tree, she was reassured when he merely remarked, "Well, well, I never saw a fox around here."

As soon as she could, Mary slipped away with her basket of darning. The lilac hedge was in bloom and the air was sweet. Something made her walk quietly as she came near the hole among the roots of the pine tree.

There, some distance away, as though they were looking for their mother, were two fox cubs. They were very little, no larger than kittens, but their eyes seemed enormous above their pointed faces. Their small red brushes hung down in the dust and they were making little hungry sounds.

Mary stole up behind them, set the basket down quickly across the hole to stop it up, and proceeded to catch the cubs. It was not difficult. One little creature tried to bite her, but it was like a kitten's nip. She held one in each hand, considering what to do. They looked back at her, bright-eyed. They were too young to be very much afraid, she thought, but she could feel their hearts beating fast against her fingers.

No, she decided, she would not take them back to the cottage. If Mr. Kennedy should inquire, it was safer for her grandfather and grandmother to know nothing about these two. Tucking the gentler one under her arm, she used her free hand to dump the sewing things onto the ground. Then carefully she put the cubs into the basket and set a stone on the cover to keep them from getting out while she ran back to the cottage.

"May I have a glass of milk, Grandma?" she asked.

"Certainly, dear," her grandmother said, surprised. "Didn't you eat your lunch?"

"I'd like it for a sort of picnic," Mary said.

She looked at her grandmother and her eyes added, "You understand, but we won't say it in words."

Suddenly her grandmother did understand.

"If you want it for a picnic, there's an empty tonic bottle on the shelf. Wouldn't it taste better if it's warm? You might use a clean rag for a cork."

Mary said, "Oh, thank you," and hurried to follow her grandmother's suggestions. In less than ten minutes she was running back toward the pine tree, careful not to pass either of the two quarries where she knew that men were working.

It took her some time to make the two cubs drink. They whimpered at the smell of the milk and reached out their sharp noses toward it, but they drew back at the touch of the milk-soaked rag. At last Mary put Bright, as she had named the more lively cub, back into the basket with the stone on top. Then she gave all her attention to the cub she called Pretty. Mary succeeded in forcing an end of the cloth between the cub's delicate jaws and getting a little milk into its mouth.

Suddenly the cub began to suck and Mary tipped the bottle so that the milk would flow easily. Pretty, however, took but little, and Bright took even less. Mary had to be satisfied to know that at least they had had something to eat. For a little while she left them in her lap, so that they would get used to her, and then she let them go.

Next day, when she caught them, they both seemed to understand about using the bottle, and drank till she could feel their little stomachs round and hard under the fur.

"That's enough! You'll make yourselves sick!" she protested at length. That day Pretty went to sleep in her lap.

After that they would come out of the burrow when

she called. By the end of a week or ten days they had lost all fear of her, and accepted her as their foster-mother. Pretty was always gentler than Bright, and Mary decided that they were sister and brother.

"You big tumbling boy!" she would pretend to scold Bright when he chased in and out of the grass, knocking Pretty over and biting her tail. But he was really Mary's favorite. She had never had playmates before. If only there had been some other child to share the fun with her, she would have been perfectly happy.

By August the young foxes were almost half grown and their games were often fast and furious. Mary was getting anxious lest they get into trouble as they grew up. Without asking any questions, her grandmother had begun to order extra bones and trimmings at the meat store, and these her grandfather patiently carried up the mountain in a basket, slung on his arm. But would these wild young creatures be satisfied?

One day the question was answered. There were chicken feathers once more at the mouth of the den.

"Oh dear! Oh dear!" cried Mary. "You bad things, you! Whatever will Mr. Kennedy do now?"

The next morning, when Mary came back to the burrow under the pine tree, the two young foxes ran out to meet her, playing about her feet, while Pretty gave little whines of welcome. They seemed to have an air at once sly and self-satisfied. At the burrow entrance there were new chicken feathers which they seemed to regard with pride.

Mary shook her head in despair as she laid out their food for them in the shade. But the cubs were not hungry. They played with their food, tasting it and dragging it about, glancing at Mary as though to say, "We can get better food than this for ourselves any time we want to now, but of course it's very kind of you to remember to bring our dinner anyway."

Suddenly, just as Bright had decided to drag a piece of meat into the burrow and Pretty had decided that it was better left outside, and they were pretending to struggle and growl and tug over it, Mary was startled by a step behind her.

She turned. There stood the tall, lean figure of Mr. Kennedy, with a gun slung over his arm, watching them.

"So that's where my chickens have gone!" he remarked grimly.

At the sound of his voice Mary jumped to her feet and the cubs disappeared down the burrow.

"I've tried to keep them from killing chickens, really and truly, Mr. Kennedy," the girl cried out. "They don't know any better. Oh, please don't kill them! They're all I have in the world."

Mr. Kennedy turned his sharp elderly gaze full upon the anxious girl.

"Well, suppose the chickens are all I have!" he said.

"A chicken isn't as much company as a fox," Mary pleaded. "Maybe if I feed them and feed them, they'll keep away. Please, please give us another chance."

"You could just as well keep a bird from a tree, as a

fox from a chicken," Mr. Kennedy declared. Then he
added to Mary, "Well, let's sit down and talk it over as
neighbors should."

Before Mary knew it she was talking to Mr. Kennedy
so earnestly that she never had time to think of herself
at all, and he was listening, his eyes on her face, nodding
now and then, but saying very little.

"Well," said Mr. Kennedy when she had quite finished,
"I don't know that I'm really so fond of raising chickens
when I come to think of it. It is more of a habit with
me than anything else. I haven't very many chickens —
about fifteen, I guess. I could sell those easy enough. Fact
is, my wife's been after me a long time to get rid of those

44

chickens. And when they're gone, your foxes will have to eat what they're given, for there aren't any other chickens anywhere around."

Mary looked at him with glowing eyes.

"You're the kindest man, Mr. Kennedy," she cried. "When I think how scared I've been of you for weeks I can hardly believe I'm awake now."

"But we haven't shaken hands, Mary, so it isn't a bargain yet," Mr. Kennedy said, while Mary's heart sank into her boots. "I have two grandchildren," he went on. "Grace must be about your age, and Danny is just a mite younger. Now they've never seen anything like this and you've got to agree to show them your foxes and try to make the cubs friends with them, too, or our bargain is off. Is that understood?"

"Why, but I'd love to!" Mary cried. "Will you shake hands then, and Bright and Pretty won't be shot?"

Mr. Kennedy solemnly stuck out his lean brown hand.

"Shake," he said, and Mary never guessed that his eyes were twinkling because he had made an agreement so that at last she might know some children and meet them on her own ground.

Next day she joined Mr. Kennedy and Grace and Danny by the pine tree at three o'clock as they had agreed. Coaxing the young foxes out of their burrow was not so easy, but at last they answered Mary's whistle, attracted by the fish-heads she had brought with her. It was a breathless moment when there was the first stir at the mouth of the earth and then a pointed red head stuck out

45

suspiciously and at last a bright soft body followed and then another joined the first.

For a little while, Bright and Pretty were fearful in the presence of strangers, but before long they became friendly and allowed Grace and Danny to feed them. At last they began playing and the game grew so fast and furious that the children laughed until they could laugh no more. Grace loved Pretty because she was gentle. Danny loved Bright because he was so gay. When finally the foxes trotted off into the underbrush, the children were chattering like old friends. No one would ever have guessed that they had known each other for only an afternoon or that they were the first friends with whom the Quarry Girl had ever played.

Almost every day the Kennedys climbed the mountain, and the children played together while Mr. Kennedy went to the red cottage to talk with Mary's grandfather. Before very long the foxes treated them all alike.

"Good!" they seemed to say. "Here are the children. That means something nice to eat, and a romp."

Soon other children came too, and before long there was a Fox Club to which it was a great honor to belong.

Mary was no longer afraid of strangers and no one pointed at her and called her "quarry girl." She had a dozen friends now and was president of the Fox Club. She knew that she was a lucky girl to have two foxes for pets and to live on the top of Mount Ararat.

Elizabeth Coatsworth

46

SANTOS, THE HORSE HUNTER

DRIVING four spare horses, one slightly lame and needing a day's rest, I rode into the Andean town of El Punto, which is crowded between the foothills and the sea. A week's rain had made the place a mud hole unfit for man or horse, but a boy herding goats at the edge of town told me about Tio Ravenna, who owned a clean pasture, and so to Tio I went. He was a good fellow. His pasture was well grassed. His house, a one-roomed, sod-built affair, was warm and dry, but very smoky because of a fire in the middle of the floor. Tio and I sat, in spite of smoke, and told our histories, talked about horses, and praised the country. Not until we were stretched on the floor to sleep did he ask me how long I intended to stay.

When I told him that I was bound for nowhere in particular, but was interested in seeing what places and people were like, he said, "It is good to be free as wild animals are. It is thus with my brother Santos. He is a horse hunter, though some call him an outlaw. No man is better with a horse. No man is more respected among Patagonian Indians."

Tio stirred the fire to make it blaze. Then he explained that Santos knew every herd of wild horses and caught many for his own use, but disliked to sell them. Usually Santos visited El Punto about this time of the year and might be expected any day.

"You could have no better companion than Santos in seeing the Andes," Tio added.

Two days later the weather had cleared, my lamed horse was sound again, and Santos himself rode in. In

front of his own mount he was driving six spare horses. They were spirited creatures with long manes and long tails, nervous eyes, and satin skins. All were fresh from the land where wild horses live.

Santos himself was short and active and wiry, not yet thirty years old. His black bristling beard grew thick, and his eyes were bright and shining and squeezed-up, as if used to looking into far distances. A typical Gaucho, Santos was not given to talk except about horses and horsemen. He had the highest praise for his two companions, Osorno and Kilal, Patagonian Indians, but no good word at all for white men. Santos said the white men did not know how to treat their horses, but counted them fit only when their spirits were broken. However, he thought my horses had been fairly treated but said it was time they were turned loose since I had owned them for more than a year. If I went with him, I could pick and choose from a hundred horses.

"Then," said Tio, "I suppose Don Carlos can ride with you and the two Patagonian lads?"

Santos made some reply in Spanish which I took to mean, "There's no doubt about it."

So began my partnership with Gaucho Santos.

It was a very good world indeed the next morning when we rode into the valley with a bright sun shining. Our driven horses were snorting and biting in play, tossing their heads and shaking their manes, leaping mountain streams and startling wild geese from their hiding places. There were hours on end when we rode at an easy trot. Santos was singing rather tunelessly a song of many verses about a Martin Fierro, who seemed to be Jesse James and Robin Hood and Daniel Boone all rolled into one.

The land through which we rode was unspoiled country where the sound of a gun had never been heard. It was a land of deer, of guanaco, of kingly condors sailing up the wind without movement of wing. It was a land of a thousand little furred and feathered creatures, of racing cloud shadows, of insects making music. Every two or three hours we rounded up our driven horses, released those we had ridden, caught others for mounts from the drive, and were on our way again.

On the evening of the second day we came to a hill from which we could see, far below, a valley of rich grass and the light of the campfire which the Indians, Osorno and Kilal, had made. On the way down we passed their two dozen horses grazing in thick grass, knee deep. We headed our driven horses to join theirs.

The next high point in the adventure was dinner with the Patagonians. We fared well on roasted ostrich breast and great pieces of cold deer meat.

For a while after eating we sat silent. The evening world was quiet except for the crackling of sticks in the fire, the soft noises made by the grazing horses, and now and then the far-off hoot of an owl. Kilal broke the silence by saying that there might be at least two hundred wild horses in a certain valley to the north.

"I know that herd well," said Santos. "There is an old bay-colored mare in it. On her side are the white hairs of a cinch mark, showing that she has been owned by white men and escaped."

"She is lucky," said Kilal. "The life of a horse among white men is not good."

"White men are fools with horses," said Santos. "They keep them in towns, where the poor creatures never see grass. They put them in houses at night. They tie them to wheeled things. They work them until they fall dead. Those are not good ways."

"The way the white man burns his mark on a horse's leg is not good, either," observed Kilal. "They do it that they may know their horses, yet I know mine without branding them. Have horses not colors, no two the same? Have they not ways of running, no two the same? And is not the face of one horse unlike the face of another?"

"And how it spoils the looks of a horse to brand him with a hot iron!" said Osorno.

They were very indignant for a while. Then, in the way of the plainsman, they suddenly found something very amusing in the white man's habits and had great fun at the white man's expense. Did the white man think he owned the world and its creatures, and would he try to brand the pumas and the deer? Did the white man brand his children so that he might know them?

So they made merry until we wrapped ourselves in our blankets and lay down to sleep. Then out of the dark boomed the voice of Santos.

"I like to see horses free. Though I have caught and sold many to white men, I have helped many to escape and to return to their native places. Because I have done so and shall do so again, they call me outlaw. Yet my heart is with the horses and I know I do right."

"Can you deny that, Don Carlos?" Kilal asked me.

How could I explain to them the rights and wrongs of private property? How could I go into the long story of discovery and ownership in South America that led back for generations? How could I tell them about the first Spaniards who landed and laid waste, then sailed away again? They would probably not believe me if I told them that these vast herds of horses that roamed from the Straits of Magellan to the equator were descended

from three mares and two horses left to run wild by the Spaniards. So I merely said that there was much to be said about the matter and went to sleep.

We came, after many leagues, to the valley where the wild horses were, a funnel-shaped opening that ran into the mountains. It was five miles wide at the pampas end but narrowed to a canyon. It was good to see the wild horses grazing quietly. They were stocky, hard-hoofed animals, fit for long journeys on scant fare, every one of them with a dash of Arab blood. They were of many colors, bays, grays, blacks, and dark browns, but very rarely whites. As we looked down on them, my companions began picking out the ones that they chose for their own, much as a man might choose a dog from a litter of puppies.

"That bay shall be mine," exclaimed Kilal. "You see it there by the little bush? That patch of white hair above the tail means a swift and strong horse with a good mouth."

"I shall have the dark brown," said Osorno. "It is a color I like, and such a horse always turns out well."

"The good God made nothing more beautiful than a horse, whatever the color," said Santos. "We shall keep no more than we can use."

"It will be easy to gather them," said Kilal.

There was no conference, no plan, but everyone seemed to know what to do. First, we gathered our spare horses on the shoulder of the hill. There was no need to drive them, for they headed willingly enough for the herd that grazed in the valley below, trotting at first. The trot became a run, and the run a swift gallop. In the valley the wild horses, moved by curiosity, gathered about them, sniffing and neighing, playing, perhaps recognizing former companions.

Then down we swept, the four of us, not making much noise, but riding so as to turn the entire herd into the valley. When they were well on the move, Kilal and I rode after the horses, urging them on. Santos took the hill on the north side, Osorno the hill on the south side so as to turn back any possible stampede of the herd. But there was no stampede, for the horses were not scared.

Before the sun went down behind the mountains we had the herd rounded up in the deep canyon with three precipitous sides, while we were camped and on watch at the mouth. The wild herd, captured unawares, was in a natural corral familiar to it, with good grass and water from a mountain stream.

Early in the morning Santos began playing the game which only Gauchos play — not every one of them, but a gifted few. He had chosen a horse and must needs try how it rode, how it acted, what sort of mouth it had, and what promise of gait and speed. So he rode hither and thither until he neared the horse he had chosen. Then

54

out flew his whirling boleadoras, not the heavy ones which would crack the head of a bull, but the light ones of hide-covered wooden balls. Cleverly thrown, this form of lasso caught the horse about the upper part of its fore-legs and down the entangled animal went.

Santos dismounted and ran to the fallen horse. Placing a knee on its neck, he freed it from the boleadoras. Then he took a six-foot strip of hide from his waist and deftly made a double hitch about the horse's jaw so that the strip served for both bit and reins. Next he got swiftly to his feet and stood over the horse. When it rose he was astride it. He urged it into a clumsy canter and brought it to us at the canyon's entrance.

It was a superb piece of horsemanship. I have not seen such elsewhere but I saw it often on the drive, because both Santos and the Patagonians caught and gentled wild horses in that fashion. Never was there sign of cruelty or of bad temper even with vicious horses. There was no whip or spur, no heedless shouting or yelling, but always a great deal of laughter on the part of both rider and onlooker.

Santos and the Patagonians were particular about what they took. The best animals they kept for their own use, but mares with foals or young colts, and horses showing signs of weakness were turned back among their wild companions. At the end we had our driven horses, those the hunters had decided to keep, and thirty medium animals which were good enough for the white man's market.

Charles J. Finger

OOTIK'S FIRST WHALE

OOTIK sat on the Baffin Island shore with the men, waiting for the coming of the white whales. It was early July, near the time for the annual migration to the cold northern waters. The whales would soon be here in great schools, frisking and leaping and spouting spirals of mist into the air. Their white bodies and tails would gleam against the water, which would be darkened by the steep, overshadowing cliffs.

Ever since he could remember, Ootik had watched each year for the coming of the white whales to Baffin Island. He used to climb high on the rocks that enclosed the bay. At first, when he was quite little, the noises which the whale hunters made to frighten and drive the whales into shallow water used to terrify him — the wild shouting of the hunters, the firing of guns, the chug-chugging of motor

boats, the rattling of oars, the pounding of drums and pans and kettles.

Usually Baffin Island was a silent land. Only once in the year, when the white whales came, and his Eskimo people took to the water to catch them, did these awful sounds disturb its quiet.

Pretty soon, Ootik was thinking, he would be twelve. At thirteen he would be old enough to row in one of the whale-boats. And what fun that would be! He imagined how the whale-boats would spread out in line like a bridge across the mouth of the bay to hold the whales inside until the tide should fall beneath the level of the sharp ledges of the bar and trap them. He could remember how the frantic creatures, frightened by the shallow water, beat against the black rocks in their struggle to escape.

"Ootik!" called his mother. "Come away. Come and help me! I have much to do before the whales come." She paused, her eyes full of anxiety. "If they come!"

Ootik rose at once and left the men on the shore. They had packed the seams of their whale-boats with fresh tar, tested the strength of their oars, and piled all the noise-making apparatus which they possessed — metal sticks, cans, drums, kettles, and whistles — in the boats ready for action. As he left, they were getting up to examine their outfits again to make sure that everything was ready for the whale-catching.

Ootik knew that his mother was not strong like the other women. Eager to help her all he could, he went with her obediently and attended to the chores which she set for him. Then he helped her sharpen her semicircular knives, the ooloos, which must be very sharp for chopping up the blubber.

Ootik felt a little of his mother's anxiety lest the whales be delayed or not come at all. This had been a bad year for his people, for the seals had been scarce and they were depending on the coming of the whales. And now his father, at a time when he was in debt at the Hudson Bay Company's trading-post, was short a man for his boat!

Ootik looked at his mother, patiently grinding her knives. She needed many things — pots, clothes, and the fine sugar and tea which the post manager had on his shelves, and which the Eskimos could afford only when the seals and whales were plentiful. It was foolish of his father to say that Ootik was not old enough to go in the boats when he could make as much noise as any of the men. Why, he could keep watch of the whales — especially that largest one that he used to look for from the cliffs, and that seemed to be the leader. For many years Ootik had watched this big whale come into the little bay.

Another day came and still there was no sight of the white whales. The long arctic day was dissolving into the bright arctic night when at last a scout came with the news that the great migration had begun. The whales were on their way in thousands. But they were still some distance off. No one knew when they would reach the bay. The tides were treacherous and the ice floes were heavier this year than usual. The hunters had reason to feel nervous and excited.

At the trading-post where Ootik was sent next morning to ask for supplies against the certainty of the big whale drive, his eyes fell enviously upon some pink cakes of scented soap. It was a long time since there had been any sweet-smelling soap in the hut of his people. He picked a cake out of the newly opened box, smelled it, and put it back.

The post manager smiled at him. "You like that soap?" he asked.

"I will buy a whole box of it when I become a whale hunter," said Ootik.

Ootik wondered if this pink soap had been made out of the whale oil which was shipped every year from Baffin Island. Whale oil was used, the post manager had told his people, to make the fine soaps which he sold. Ootik longed to know how the soap-makers were able to turn the oil into such fine-smelling soap — soap which cleaned the dirt off the hands so quickly. It seemed funny to him. He wondered if his people would ever learn to make soaps themselves.

In a few days now, thought Ootik, if all went well, his mother and the other women would be working at great speed with their ooloos, stripping the blubber from the hides of the whales which the men would spread upon the great wooden platform near the post.

The men would pack this blubber into drums, to be cut up later by the women and put through a grinder. The ground-up fat would then be placed in vats in the sun, or over slow fires, until it had melted into clear oil. This oil would be poured into the thousands of barrels which were now stacked up at the post waiting for it. Later these would be shipped south to the soap-makers.

Ootik, looking at the shelves full of goods at the trading-post, wished greatly that he could have asked right away for a cake of the pink soap. There were other things he saw which he longed for. For instance, there was a shirt with broad checks, like his father's, and a silk handkerchief, rich in color, that would suit his mother. There was a shawl, too, that would be good for her now that it was too warm for her sealskin coat.

Having completed his errand, Ootik went again to the shore, where the men waited almost overcome with excitement and uncertainty. They were anxiously watching the ice floes which the wind was tossing furiously about beyond the mouth of the bay. Some smaller cakes of ice were coming into the quiet waters of the fiord.

Only fifty men were on hand for the whale-killing. There ought to be more. But so urgent had been the need for food that many of the younger hunters had gone off after seals, hoping to be back before the whales arrived. The men kept their eyes on the sharp-toothed ledges which the rising tide would soon cover. If the whales should show up now, the hunters could not row out after them until the ledges were covered.

The men were worried. Ootik remembered that every year the men talked the same way. They were full of anxiety until the white whales came plunging through the sea. Then their uneasiness left them. They sprang to their boats and were off, the danger of ice floes forgotten. Ootik knew he, too, would be uneasy until he saw the whales.

The men continued to argue. Ootik was thinking hard, thinking of the prosperity which the white whales would bring to his people. But he felt worried about his father, who was short a man, for the young man who belonged in his boat was off with the seal hunters. Ootik remembered the desirable articles that lay upon the shelves of the trading-shop — the plaid shirt, the bright-colored handkerchief, the warm light shawl, the cakes of pink soap.

Stowaway

It was not until the next day that the whales came leaping and piling from the outer water into the quiet haven of the bay. Through the ice floes came thousands of the white creatures, pounding and thrashing in their northward drive.

The boats were drawn to the edge of the water, ready to push off. The men sat down to wait. The tide was turning, but it would be some time before it covered the black ledges. This would be a great day! If only the hunters who had gone after seals were here!

Ootik stole away from the men and went along the shore to his father's boat. The tin utensils for noise-making and the sails and spears were piled close against the stern of the boat. Over them was thrown a skin covering. Ootik crept under the robe.

He would have to lie hidden here for a long time, he thought, until the tide was right. Close by, his mother was calling him. He gave no answer. She would keep

on looking for him, he knew, to help her with her chores.
He was sorry to cause her worry, but what he was about
to do now would help them all.

The hot arctic noon sun was beating full into the boat.
It was suffocating under the robe, but he was afraid to put
his head out lest someone passing discover him. Once the
boats had pushed off, all would be well.

Meanwhile, the whales were gamboling in the shadows of the cliffs and breathing and spouting the water in great spirals of mist high in the air. They were not far from the rocky ledges. The men waited impatiently.

"The ledges are covered! No! They are yet bare!" the men kept repeating. "See! There is still black rock showing! Now is the time! Not yet!" At last they all spoke together. "Now the water is flowing over the bar!"

With glad cries, the men ran to their boats and jumped in. The happy cries and commands of the boatmen were music to Ootik. Soon his father and his men were pulling on their oars with great strokes, sending the heavy whaleboat with speed through the ice floes. Ootik lifted a corner of the robe and looked out. The backs of the rowers were toward him. Across the open mouth of the little bay, some of the boats were already in line forming a bridge — a man-made trap — to prevent the whales from escaping to the open sea. Ootik's father swung his boat into position near the middle of the line.

Not far from the ledges, the whales thrashed about and blew and leaped. Picking up a stout tin can and a wooden stick, Ootik threw off the skin robe and said, "I can help with the noise, Father. You need another man!" His father had no time to show surprise or to argue. The whales had turned and were coming straight at the boats.

Immediately there was a great blast of sound. The hunters sprang up in their boats, firing guns, yelling, beating on their tins, and blowing their whistles. The noise was deafening. The shining white creatures, baffled, turned back to the ledges dividing the bay, where they swam about. Then they came straight at the boats again. Again the noise met them and turned them back to the ledges.

The tide, Ootik saw, was at its height. It was turning. Soon the men would try to drive the whales over the ledges and keep them there until the water fell low enough to trap them in the shallow lagoon on the other side.

Ootik kept his eyes on one large whale which he recognized as the leader. When the creature made a dive under water, Ootik lost sight of him, but was soon able to pick him out again, he was so large. Suddenly this whale was coming at the boats again, leading the school. Now the school was dividing. One group made for the end of the line of boats where, in spite of the shots and shouting of the hunters, it dove under the boats and escaped to open water. This division of the school confused the boatmen in the center of the line of boats. For a second all, including Ootik's father, were off guard.

But Ootik had not lost sight of the leader. The big whale had turned back and was preparing to dive under his father's boat.

"Stop him! Shoot!" cried Ootik.

His father and the men turned in time to send volley after volley of shells into the water. The big whale and his followers rushed toward the ledges and over.

Without ceasing their noise, the hunters drew their boats nearer the ledges. The tide was falling quickly. In fifteen minutes, perhaps a little less, the rocky teeth would be in sight. Then the white whales would be fast in a trap.

"Good boy! Good son! You saved the whales!" Ootik's father told him. Ootik heard his father's words, but he did not take his eyes off the leader, who was thrashing about in the water. The boy blew his whistle and beat the cans without stopping until the black ledges were well out of water.

The hunters were a happy lot. They put down their noise-making tools. They stopped shouting. Wealth for

the year was in the lagoon. They rushed forward to spear and kill the stranded whales before the tide should rise again and carry them off.

"I will go home," said Ootik.

His father put him ashore before going to join in the killing and cutting up.

Later on, after the whales had been cut up and the blubber melted into oil and sold at the trading-post, the Eskimo people had a great feast. When all was ready, an old whale hunter rose and spoke. "We give honor to the quick eye and the quick tongue of Ootik! If he had not turned the big whale back, we should go hungry this year. We accept Ootik as a whale hunter."

All the people at the feast clapped their hands and sang an Eskimo "thank-you" song.

Then Ootik's father rose. He said, "All the blubber from the big whale that Ootik saved for us, I sold at the post. This is the money I received for it. That money is for Ootik." He held it out to his son.

Ootik made a stiff little bow and managed to say, "I am glad I helped my people."

The people clapped and clapped and clapped. When they grew quiet, Ootik slipped away from the feast and ran as fast as his legs would carry him to the trading-post. He burst into the shop a little breathlessly. Pointing to the handkerchief, the shawl, the plaid shirt, and the big box of pink soap, he said, "I will take that and that and that and that."

Mary Weekes

67

GINGER FOLLOWS THE TRAIL

GINGER behaved as well as a dog could while waiting for Sue and Sue's father to collect the mail and the news from the mailman. Ginger could not help being restless, for she had a good many things on her mind, including her puppies, which were growing fast and getting out of hand. But she would not dream of missing a trip to the mailbox, because it was her job to carry home the daily newspaper.

Sue and her father did not start back to the house as promptly as usual after the mailman had driven off. Mr. Brenn stopped and opened a letter which he read aloud. Ginger did not pay much attention because she had her eye on a bumblebee across the road. Suddenly, however, the dog pricked up her ears at the sound of her own name.

". . . Ginger, I understand (ran the letter), had some puppies a while ago. I need a dog badly out here and Airedales are rare in this neck of the woods. Could you let me have Ginger, since there are so many other dogs on your place? I suggest that you take a vacation from Ohio and your farm and come out to Kansas and my ranch for a fortnight, if possible, and bring along the dog. Take the train to Dorado, where I'll be coming to buy a flock of ewes. We'll drive them back together. Ginger would be mighty useful herding the sheep on the way and afterward."

Ginger's eyes were shining and her tail was thumping at being talked about in a tone that she knew was complimentary.

"Your uncle is right," said Mr. Brenn. "Ginger would be useful. Airedales are hard to beat for good sense."

"But I don't want Ginger to go to Uncle Lloyd's!" wailed Sue. "She belongs here. She was born here. She doesn't know any other place but Ohio. She wouldn't like Kansas, and the people out there wouldn't understand her ways. You'd be miserable, wouldn't you, Ginger?"

Ginger stood still, wagging her stump of a tail and regarding Sue with her head a little on one side. She was trying to understand.

"You forget," said Mr. Brenn, "that I'll be there too for a while. By the time I leave for home, she'll be used to the place and people. Besides, Sue, you will have her four puppies to train. They're old enough to get along without their mother now."

Sue knew it was no use to say anything more. She leaned down and put the folded newspaper between Ginger's teeth and the three set out for the house.

At the front door, Ginger dropped the paper on the top step and wagged her satisfaction at a good job well done. Mr. Brenn picked up the paper and went in.

Sue and Ginger went on to the high, wired kennel where four lively young copies of Ginger crowded around the gate. They were pawing at the wire fence and at one another. The gate clicked open at Sue's touch. Out the puppies tumbled, giving little yelps and barks, twisting and turning and showing their teeth in their young mirth, rushing away and rushing back, eager for the coming fun.

Down the road, past the mailbox, across the wide field to the river the pups tore, playing with the clumsy grace of young animals. Ginger was more sober, as became a parent, but she made her own little excursions, returning now and then to Sue with tail wagging and teeth showing in a dog grin.

Mr. Brenn, watching Sue with the dogs, stroked his chin and said to himself, "It's too bad we have to let Ginger go. I wish Lloyd could wait for us to train a puppy, but that's impossible."

A week later Ginger peered unhappily at a tearful Sue from the crate in which she was confined at the railroad station. Then she was lifted into the baggage car and the train moved off. The dog had no way of knowing whether hours or days of semidarkness followed. Occasionally Mr. Brenn came to her and spoke words of encouragement, only to disappear again. Once by daylight and once under bright night lights he took her out on a station platform for a run on a leash, but each time she was returned to the baggage car. As the hours dragged on, her nervousness increased with the rattling and banging and whistling and thumping all around her.

At last Mr. Brenn's kindly hands released her and she emerged, a free dog, into the sunshine. For the remainder of that day Ginger hardly left her master's side.

The next morning she was too busy to realize where she was or how she felt, for Mr. Brenn and his brother began

driving the new flock of sheep to the ranch, and for several days Ginger was a very busy dog.

At the ranch everything was new and strange to her, but Ginger did not mind, for Mr. Brenn was never far away and often stopped to give her an encouraging word or a pat.

Then came the day when, standing in the barn doorway with the hired man's hand linked through her collar, she saw Mr. Brenn drive off in a car. Ginger gave a mighty leap but could not wrench away from the hand through her collar. She raised her nose into the air and uttered a mournful cry.

"Better chain her up until she gets thoroughly used to the place," remarked Uncle Lloyd to the hired man.

Ginger's world now went wholly awry. Why should she, who had always been free, be confined by chain and collar? Where were the people she knew and loved? Where were the friendly sheep and the girl who laughed and teased and threw a hard rubber ball that was fun to find? Where, above all, were her puppies?

In the night, Ginger's grief changed to anger. She pulled at her chain and shook it. Then, slowly, she backed away from the box stall where she was tied until the chain was taut. When one ear had worked under the collar until it hurt, she whimpered a little and rested a while. She backed again, felt the collar pressing her throat, lowered her head to lessen the pain, and, still backing, gave a tug and a wriggle. At last chain and collar fell off and she was free.

After that there was no hesitation for Ginger. She was off for home. The right way for her was the way she had come with those strange sheep. For a while the trail was easy. She recognized a post here, a mesquite bush there, a tree elsewhere, though she did not expect them. When she happened to come to them, she knew them. She felt her way along. If she went a wrong way, as she did at a place where crossroads met and the sheep had scattered, she was uncomfortable until she hit again on the right trail. The few times she made a wrong turn, she went back and forth until she found something she had seen on the westward journey. Before the day was over, she had gained something of a sense of general direction.

It was the right and comfortable way when she came to the place where, two weeks earlier, the sheep had camped for the night. There she rested a while. She lapped eagerly at the bubbling spring. She nosed about the place where the sheep had slept. She even found the spot where she had buried a bone and unearthed it. Everything was right, then, because it was familiar.

On the second day of her homeward trek, the roadway ran parallel to a railroad which she remembered well. Terrible, roaring, earth-shaking things passed along that way. Each time she crouched low in the long grass.

When the sun stood high she saw a group of men, sitting and eating, close to the place where the great and terrible things sometimes ran. She approached the group warily. But in the voice of one of the men was friendliness as he threw her a piece of bread. Then, seeing her eat it greedily, he offered more. This time he held the bread in his hand. Ginger sniffed a couple of inches from the offered food, but her suspicions came to an end when she smelled dog on the man. When she had eaten the bread, the man put out his hand and said words that she knew, "Shake hands." She lifted a paw and allowed it to be gripped. Now again, the world was good indeed. Other hands gave her scraps. Since the way for a dog to thank a man is to lick his hand, she did so.

Then the men lifted the seat on which they had been sitting, put it on the rails where the noisy monsters ran, and went away with a great clanking and rattling.

The days of travel worked a change in Ginger. Her coat lost its gloss and burrs tangled her hair. She became thin and ragged and lost something of that look of high pride which had so delighted Sue.

Once, with a locust thorn in her paw, she limped for miles on three legs until a whistling boy saw her and called her to him. That he was friendly there could be no doubt at all, so she went to him without fear. He, still whistling softly, took her paw and did something which hurt for a moment but left her whole-footed again. She looked up at him with grateful eyes, and he said something which was clearly an invitation to follow. For a moment she hesitated, then went trustfully to heel.

They came to a house where he poured out milk for

her and gave her food. Afterwards he shut her in a wood-shed, but with kind words and gentle hand. When he had gone, it was easy to nose open the unlatched door and step into the sunlight and listen to friendly noises that she understood — the clucking of a hen with chicks, the distant cow bell, the sound of a far-off ax, and the voice of a woman calling. There was even a girl child near the house, but when Ginger went toward her, the child ran away.

Day by day Ginger went on with the sun behind her, following her shadow. That was the comfortable way — to trot toward the sun in the morning, to sleep when it was high, to follow her shadow after the noonday sleep. Also, going that way she came to places with a familiar look, places where they had camped, once to a farm where they had stayed for a night.

The time came when there were no more familiar places, and she found herself where houses were closer and closer together, where no grass grew, where the earth gave way

to stone that was sun-baked. There were people coming and going in great numbers, and wheels and wheels and wheels, and strange unpleasant smells, and unfriendly dogs that snapped, snarled, bared their teeth, and were eager for quarrel. The high sun overhead made her weary, but she could find no place in which to curl up and sleep. A hundred thousand footsteps confused her, and she had to go warily and doubtfully. She sought quiet passages between houses. Her tongue hung out with thirst.

It was good to come to a place where a cart horse drank from a trough, and she could rise on her hind legs, lean over, and lap eagerly. When the horse had finished drinking, she heard the driver cluck. The cart turned and went the comfortable way, and so Ginger ran out and followed under the wheels in the moving shade.

Presently they came to a halt. The man got down from the cart and called to Ginger, patted her head and examined her, talking the while to a woman who stood on the steps of the house.

That night there was comfort for Ginger in the stable with the horse, and she slept well in the sweet-smelling hay. When the gray light of morning came she was off and away toward the sun, light on her feet after the night's good rest.

It was a pleasant day until noon. Then a distant rolling of thunder brought her to a stand, fearful of danger, perplexity in her eyes. Neither barn nor kennel was near, nor a house under which she could crawl. Another crashing roll sounded. With a cry she fled to cover and darkness.

She found a partly hollow tree, where she lay curled into herself, battered by rain, deafened by thunder, trembling with fear until a great silence came and birds began to twitter. Then her trembling fear was gone in a flash and she was strong again, eager to find that place to which she belonged, the world where all was right.

Now there was clinging mud, and creeks brimming from bank to bank where rushing waters swept her off her feet. When the sun dropped she was footsore and weary, almost too tired to lick the caked mud from her feet. She slept uneasily, for her legs twitched with sudden jerks and woke her time and time again. When the sun rose, she got up with an effort, stood swaying for a while, then lay down again for a space.

While she lay, there came from a near-by farmhouse a small boy who said soothing words and put his arms about her neck. She felt a grateful sense of companionship and forgot her trouble. Then the boy stood up and called her to follow, and led the way to the house where a woman brought food.

Ginger ate while boy and woman watched. There were sights and sounds most pleasing in that place — cows, lowing calves, clucking hens, noisy guinea fowls, and white grunting pigs. There was a collie, too, sharp-nosed and playful. Soon Ginger was well rested and clean, for she licked herself while resting. She might have stayed here happily, but again the call to find the home beyond the hills came to her and she went on.

Often, that day, Ginger sought for something familiar

without reward, but she kept on the east and home-bound trail. She was guided by a kind of "in-wit," as are birds of passage through the trackless air, or as salmon are when they pass from ocean to river, then presently back to sea. Her course was not compass-straight, but like the way of a sailing vessel forced at times to tack against a wind. Often, puzzled in tall grass or high-weeded places, she leaped high to see, for a dog's horizon is narrow, as needs must be for eyes that are but three hand's-breadths above the earth.

One day, thus leaping, she saw an iron tower, and at the sight she seemed suddenly to enter a friendly world. Straight for it she headed. A scramble up a steep bank brought her to the iron framework of a bridge. She gave a little bark that was half growl and set off at a swift run down the road, raising dust and uttering eager yelps as if she called. Soon the yelps became barkings as she recognized her world, the real world, the world of which she was a very part, with bushes, trees, stones, fences all familiar as things should be.

The sound of that barking reached the ears of a man who stood holding a gate open for some sheep. He looked down the road where Ginger was raising the dust, then put his hands to his mouth, trumpet-fashion, and shouted, "Oh, Sue! Sue! Hurry! It's Ginger come home! Come on, Ginger! Good girl, Ginger!"

Out of the house came Sue, with puppies at her heels. She took the porch steps with a leap, and they with a scramble, and, for them all, the world became splendid.

Charles J. Finger

DAYDREAMS

HIKE TO THE HILLS

Sᴍᴏᴋʏ with buds, the woods along the sky
Stand quickened in the pouring blue of night,
And in the wild brook meadows first frogs cry
And on the steep road cherry trees blow white.

All day we've followed Spring while she sped on
From hill to valley, up to that high range
Where hollows are filled with snow though Winter's
　gone —
We've followed Spring, the beautiful and strange,

Up slopes of tender green, through misty trees,
While crows beat north in dark, hoarse-throated flight.
We dream no hours lovelier than these
As we descend to village candlelight.

Frances Frost

WISHES

It would be a fine thing
To be flying, to be flying under a cool moon,
As a point of an arrow of wings loosed to the north,
To be a great gray Canada goose flying under the moon
Honking high among the winds.

It would be a fine thing
To be a sailor, measuring a ship with his eye,
Carrying his suitcase down to a fo'castle locker,
Hearing the water slap-slap-slapping at the sides of a vessel,
Shaping a yarn in his mind.

Elizabeth Coatsworth

A SONG OF GREATNESS

(From the Chippewa)

WHEN I hear the old men
Telling of heroes,
Telling of great deeds
Of ancient days,
When I hear that telling
Then I think within me
I, too, am one of these.

When I hear the people
Praising great ones,
Then I know that I, too,
Shall be esteemed.
I, too, when my time comes
Shall do mightily.

Mary Austin

83

IN A TREE

A BRANCH can be a lot of things,
    A branch can be a boat,
With leafy waves around its prow,
    To keep the ship afloat.

A branch can be a picnic place,
    With fruit already there,
And shelves of green to keep the buns
    From falling through the air.

A branch can be a meeting place,
    To which a squirrel will come
If you are good at keeping still,
    And he's adventuresome.

A branch can be a thinking place,
    With quiet all around,
And over you the arching sky,
    And under you the ground.

                              Marchette Chute

WITH SKILL AND PLUCK

THE RUNAWAY PLANE

Above the steady throb of the seaplane motor sounded the faint dismal howling of a dog. Lawson Hale, of Midwest Skyways, Inc., frowned as he looked toward the rear cockpit, which held a young Airedale he was transporting to northern Michigan for a friend. The sound, faint though it was, was getting on the pilot's nerves. It seemed to him that the dog had been howling at two-minute intervals ever since they had taken off from Chicago.

Lawson glanced downward at the misty blue expanse of Lake Michigan. The lake at that point appeared deserted. Far to the west, where the Wisconsin shore was almost out of sight, a solitary vessel was moving to the north.

The dog paused for a few seconds as if for breath. Then the dismal howling began again, more loudly now.

"Believe me," Lawson said to himself, "the next time a friend asks me to do him a favor like this — now what's the matter?"

The motor had suddenly lost its steady rhythm. Lawson listened with head cocked on one side, his blue eyes anxious. Yes, the motor was complaining. There was a harsh, uneven sound to it. "The only thing to do is to check up," he decided.

He cut off the power and headed the seaplane down gradually. In a few minutes the plane was on the water,

86

riding the waves. The dog back there in the cockpit was silent now.

Removing helmet, goggles, and gloves, Lawson climbed out onto one of the pontoons. The plane rose and fell. The cold water washed up around his ankles.

From the rear cockpit came a scratching sound, then a friendly pleading yelp. The young man suddenly forgot that he had been annoyed. "Poor fellow!" he murmured and edged over to lift a section of the covering of the cockpit. There on the floor sat the dog, wriggling and beating his stump of a tail from side to side.

Lawson's lips twitched into a smile. "Listen to me, Buster! Next time Jack Kenyon, or anybody else, asks me to transport a dog, the answer is no! Understand?"

Buster beat his tail more vigorously. He seemed to approve.

It took Lawson less than five minutes to discover a broken wire leading to the ignition. At the end of another five minutes he had repaired it. Standing upon the pontoon, he reached into the forward cockpit and threw open the switch. Now to crank the motor! He edged forward and, seizing a blade of the propeller, jerked it downward. Zip! The motor roared and the plane raced ahead. Too fast! He made his way back to the cockpit and throttled the motor. That was better!

He was about to climb back into the cockpit when a wave somewhat larger than any of the others struck the plane broadside. The next instant, before he knew what had happened, he was in the water.

It was several seconds before he came to the surface. As his head rose out of water, the first thing he saw was his plane speeding away from him. Here he was in Lake Michigan, clad in heavy flying clothes, at least a dozen miles from land, with not a soul aware of his danger! Treading water, he tugged at his heavy clothes.

A wave spilled over him, forcing him down, down into the blue-green depths. He struggled to the surface again. Above the sound of the waves he could hear the throbbing motor, steady, powerful — and somewhat louder. Then

he saw the plane again. To his surprise, it was moving, not in a straight northerly course, but northeast! And suddenly he understood the reason: just before he had landed, he had pushed the rudder to the right in order to head directly into the waves. That meant the plane would continue to move in a great circle until the supply of gasoline was gone — a matter of at least six hours. He groaned. If only the motor would fail! But he could expect no such good luck as that. His only chance was to swim and try to intercept the plane.

Lawson was beginning to feel the effects of the cold water and of his efforts to keep afloat. With awkward fingers he tugged at the buttons of his flying jacket. At last he had them loose. But the wet leather clung to his body, seeming to defy his attempts to free himself of it. Finally he yanked one arm out of the sleeve. A moment later he had the other arm free and saw the jacket slowly sink. Next he tried to rid himself of his shoes.

That proved to be difficult. Again and again he went under water, as his fingers struggled with the laces. His great fear now was that he might pull a lace into a knot that he never could untie. He came to the surface, puffing, half-strangled. It took a few moments for him to catch his breath, then under he went once more.

At last one shoe was off! But he had done the very thing that he had dreaded: he had pulled the lacing on the other shoe into a hard knot. Could he swim with one shoe on? Not very well. He must have a last try. Down he went, his knee updrawn. Catching his fingers in the lacing, he straightened his leg and pulled with all his remaining strength. To his joy he felt the lacing snap.

Up again, then under once more! Now both feet were free, but he had swallowed a great amount of water, and his struggle had taken much of his strength. He turned over on his back, floating, resting. The steady throb of the motor beat upon his ears as the runaway plane continued on its wide circular course.

Lawson closed his eyes. He moved his hands gently, just enough to keep his body afloat. The minutes passed.

By and by Lawson began to tread water again. He felt stronger, and with strength came a kind of confidence. He studied the course of the plane. It was east of him; if he were to swim south, he might be able to catch it.

He began to swim with strong overhand strokes, his eyes on the plane. It came nearer, nearer. He quickened his strokes. Nearer — nearer! Just a few more yards! He had a feeling of triumph. He had timed its approach correctly.

Suddenly, as he reached for the rear end of a pontoon, a strong puff of wind caught the ship and thrust it from him. With a feeling of despair, he saw it glide past him, just out of reach. Away it went, the motor throbbing. And now, as if sensing the presence of a man so near at hand, the dog began to howl again. A moment later a shaggy head appeared above the rear cockpit. Catching sight of the pilot in the water, the dog gave a leap toward him. His body hung for an instant on the edge of the cockpit. Then, with a yelp and wriggle, he was in the water.

As Buster swam close to him, Lawson lay back and floated wearily. Disappointment had struck him hard. With eyes closed, he remained motionless save for the slight movement of his hands. The sound of the motor grew fainter . . . fainter . . . The waves rose and fell.

Now the sound of the motor was becoming louder

again. Suddenly rousing for another attempt, Lawson began to tread water once more. There was the plane against the eastern horizon, bobbing gracefully as it moved southward on its circular course. He tried to estimate the distance and the speed at which the craft was moving. Then, with the dog following him, he began to swim.

He had taken not more than a dozen strokes when he felt a queer tightening in the muscles in the calves of both legs. He kicked harder, but was unable to rid the muscles of their tightness. Now the gliding ship was within fifty yards of him. If he should miss it this time, he knew there would be no strength left for a third attempt. He increased the speed of his strokes. Oh, he couldn't possibly miss it! It was only a score of yards away now.

Suddenly it was as if a powerful hand seized the calf of his right leg and pulled the muscles up into a painful knot. A wave broke over him, filling his mouth, his nose, his throat. His head went under. He tried to kick, but now there was a cramp also in the other leg.

Something touched the side of his face. He reached up, and his fingers closed upon the shaggy neck of the dog. Lawson's head came out of water again. He breathed clear air. For a second or two he forgot the pain in his knotted muscles. There was the plane gliding past him hardly a dozen feet away. Buster began to swim toward it.

Clinging with one hand to the wiry hair on the dog's neck, Lawson made rapid strokes with his free hand. He even managed to kick again, again! Two yards from the gliding plane he lunged desperately toward the near pontoon — and missed it! Again he lunged, this time with both hands. His reaching fingers touched the smooth wet wood, slid along it — farther, farther until they came to a slanting upright. He had won! With teeth clenched, he clung to the upright. After a few seconds he succeeded in getting a leg over the partly submerged pontoon.

In the wake of the moving plane the dog swam bravely on alone, but his was a losing fight. The distance between him and the plane increased swiftly.

It was a matter of several minutes before the muscles in Lawson's legs relaxed enough so that he could pull

himself up onto the plane. Standing unsteadily on the pontoon, he clung with one hand to the edge of the cockpit and with the other reached forward and shut off the motor. The plane rocked and swayed. There was a buzzing in his head and a pounding in his ears, but he managed to hang on until the feeling passed.

The dog! Where was the dog? The pilot turned his head and peered anxiously toward the rear. At first he saw nothing except heaving blue water. Then, as a big wave broke, he saw a dark speck in the midst of the foam. It was Buster!

Lawson shouted, "Come on, boy! Come on, Buster, old fellow!" His voice was weak and wavering. After a few seconds he shouted again, "Keep it up, Buster! Come on, old boy!"

Perhaps the wind carried the encouraging words to Buster's ears. Onward the dog came, now on the crest of a wave, now hidden in the trough, until Lawson had a clear view of the friendly brown eyes.

"Good old Buster! That's the boy!"

The dog was almost exhausted as Lawson, clinging with one hand to the upright, bent down and passed an arm under the quivering body. Somehow he managed to lift the poor creature. Somehow he succeeded in getting him into the forward cockpit — and there Buster lay with paws outstretched. As Lawson climbed in after him, the brown eyes blinked wearily, the water-soaked stump of a tail stirred, beat once or twice from side to side, then was still.

Poor fellow! The pilot swallowed hard. "Buster," he said abruptly between chattering teeth, "I must own you — at any price!"

Again the dog blinked his eyes and moved his stump of a tail. He seemed to approve.

Five minutes later the plane was in the air.

It was evening when Lawson Hale called his friend Jack Kenyon on the telephone. Near by on the floor lay Buster, his paws outstretched.

"Jack, this is Lawson. Yes, I'm here in town, and Buster is with me. But — er — I want to tell you something, Jack. I must own that dog. Absolutely! I'll pay you any price you ask, but — all right, I'll tell you why!"

In short, quick sentences he gave an account of his adventure and of the dog's important part in it. "I tell you, Jack, if it hadn't been for Buster, I'd probably still be out there in the middle of Lake Michigan. At the bottom of it, in fact. So I must have that dog! How about it?"

From the other end of the wire came Jack Kenyon's laughing voice, "All right, old man, you needn't be so emphatic. He's yours!"

On the floor Buster stirred, blinked his eyes, and moved his stump of a tail. Once more he seemed to approve.

Russell Gordon Carter

RACING A THUNDERSTORM

SHIRLEY CARLYLE was afraid of thunderstorms, terribly afraid. When a girl worries about possible thunderstorms more than she looks forward to the joys of a summer at camp, something is wrong.

For the first week at Camp Asquam, Shirley was blissfully happy. The days were clear and cool, without a trace of a thunderhead. She liked the girls in her tent, and they liked her, and they all felt sure that their counselor, Miss Evans, was the nicest in camp.

At the end of the first week, the weather changed and grew rapidly hotter. The next day was scorching. The usual afternoon hike was canceled because of the heat and the threatening clouds. By four nearly everybody had gathered at the bungalow. In spite of the weather, some of the girls were tramping around the porch, while still others were dancing. One group was planning a tent show, and a few girls were writing letters at the desks on the open balcony. Shirley was curled up with a book in a window seat.

A girl who had been sitting on the porch poked her head in the door. "There's a peach of a storm coming up," she shouted over the dance music.

The campers poured out on the porch to look.

"Come on out, Shirley," called one of her tentmates.

"I want to finish this story," answered Shirley, as she

pretended to be deep in a book of which she had not turned one page in the past fifteen minutes.

Just then a terrific flash, followed instantly by thunder, sent the girls flying back into the bungalow. From across the room Miss Evans saw Shirley jump to her feet with a look of terror.

The deluge of rain which followed kept Miss Evans busy for a time attending to windows. Then, as she started some group games, she looked around for Shirley but did not see her anywhere in the room.

Presently Miss Evans slipped away to hunt for the girl. She looked in the balcony, the rooms running off it, even the kitchen, in a vain search. She stood on the edge of the porch and called in the direction of the tents scattered through the grove. Miss Evans, with a look at her white shoes and the puddles, was about to step off

the porch after one last call, when the door of a closet opened and out came a pale, trembling Shirley.

"What under the sun — " began Miss Evans. She stopped as she saw the expression, almost of despair, on the girl's face. "Do you mind thunderstorms so much?" she asked.

Shirley nodded, unable to speak.

"Has your house ever been struck by lightning?" was the next question.

"No, it's just my nerves," said Shirley. "Mother and I are just alike. We are both terribly scared of thunderstorms."

"Oh!" said Miss Evans in a flat tone. Then she went on with her questioning. "Do you always choose a hot, dark closet as a place in which to spend a thunderstorm?" she asked.

"Mother and I go into her bedroom if it's a bad storm and pull down the curtains and turn on the lights and wait," Shirley answered.

"Do you do anything while you wait?"

"Sometimes we read or play games, but if it's a very bad storm we just lie down and close our eyes and wait until it's over. Sometimes we just shake all the time."

"It gets worse each year, doesn't it?"

"Yes, it does," admitted Shirley.

"That's the worst of a fear," said Miss Evans, "the way it grows. But I think you could get over this one if you tried."

"Oh, do you really?" cried Shirley.

"If you can conquer a fear just once, it will go away. I know, because I had a fear."

Shirley looked up at Miss Evans in surprise.

"You? I can't imagine your being afraid of anything."

"I was though, terribly afraid. I used to be so frightened of speaking in public, even of just making an announcement at a class meeting, that my heart seemed to come right up into my throat. I decided to conquer that fear by taking part in a public debate. I dreaded the debate every minute of the weeks I was preparing for it, but I made up my mind that I simply would not show a bit of fear when the time came. And do you know, when I began to speak, I knew right away I was going to be able to get through it. The next time I was less scared. The time after that, a little less still. And before long, I was actually enjoying debating. That's how I know that if you can conquer a fear just once, it will go away."

There came at this moment a last swift, jagged flash above the treetops. Shirley jumped.

"You see I can't help it," she wailed.

"Of course you can, if you use your common sense. As a matter of fact, you're much more likely to be run over by an automobile than you are to be struck by lightning. But I don't suppose you tremble every time you cross Main Street, do you?"

"Why, of course not," replied Shirley.

"The thing for you to do in a thunderstorm," went on Miss Evans, "is to forget it. Use sense, of course. If you're caught out-of-doors, keep away from the only tree in an open field. If you're indoors, find something to do, and do it."

"I'll try," promised Shirley. "I really will."

For several weeks there were no thunderstorms. The weather was perfect. Rowing practice began, and everybody was tried out.

Now rowing was one of the most important sports at Shirley's camp. Everyone took part, for it was the highest camp honor to be chosen a member of one of the two first crews. These would compete in the races on the lake on Crew Day at the end of the season. After three weeks' practice, the girls were saying Shirley was certain of a place on a first crew, because Miss Allerton was putting her in so often as stroke. Then suddenly she was dropped almost entirely from crew practice.

It was all on account of a thunderstorm.

The storm came up suddenly, just at suppertime. Shirley, whose seat faced the windows, had watched it come. At the first sharp flash, she jumped to her feet, gave a hoarse little scream, and ran trembling to a corner. At Miss Evans's crisp call, "Shirley!" she pulled herself together, and came back to the table, much ashamed.

Miss Allerton, the camp director, told Shirley the next day that it would not be fair to put on a crew, especially in the position of stroke, a girl whose self-control might fail her in a race.

Shirley thought her heart would break. To come so near being on a crew and then to fail!

"If I could get over being afraid of thunderstorms, would I have a chance to be on a crew?" she asked.

"Perhaps," answered Miss Allerton.

"I'm going to try," said Shirley.

If anyone had told Shirley at the beginning of the summer that the time would come when she would long for a thunderstorm, she would have thought the idea absurd. Now the longing to win a place on a crew and the respect of the girls was even greater than her fear of thunderstorms. But just when she wanted to test herself, she had no opportunity.

Four days passed with cloudless skies. Then, one midnight, a thunderstorm broke. Shirley was first of her tent to be out tightening the ropes, and in making the tent secure against a blow.

Next morning Miss Evans took Shirley aside.

"I knew you could do it," she said.

Shirley hung her head. "But I shook all over when I got back into bed," she confessed.

"Never mind," said Miss Evans. "It was a step forward to get up and attend to the ropes. Next time you may take another step."

"But next time may be too late for crews," said Shirley.

A Chance to Win

Two more days passed by. The third was the last possible day for the announcement of crews, the girls had figured. Nobody but Miss Allerton knew whether the announcement would be made at morning or at evening Pow-wow, the general get-together of the whole camp twice each day.

No one was late for Pow-wow that morning.

"I have some special announcements to make today," began Miss Allerton.

A sigh of anticipation ran round the room.

"The weather is so promising," went on the director, a mischievous gleam in her eye, "that — we shall take some of the longer hikes and rows."

The sigh turned to one of disappointment.

Miss Allerton went on rapidly reading lists of the girls who were to hike or row in various directions. "Miss Evans will take Shirley Carlyle and the three D's by boat to Carey's Island," she read.

The three D's were the youngest children in camp — Doris and Dorothy, twins, aged eleven, and Dee, just ten. They were all roly-poly, jolly youngsters, so that with them and Miss Evans and the fun of being stroke for the fifteen-minute pull to the island, Shirley had a happy morning. After lunch on the shore, they explored the island. Nobody noticed time or weather until suddenly Miss Evans, after a glance upward, declared that it was late, and they must go back to the boat.

Shirley looked at her watch. Only three o'clock! But wasn't it dark! The sun came out a moment later, but when they reached the shore, they found dark clouds piling up rapidly on the horizon.

Miss Evans looked anxious. Nevertheless, her voice was cheerful as she said briskly, "Pile everything in. I think we can make it." She stepped into the boat as she spoke.

Shirley made no move to obey. She stood stock-still on the shore, staring at the angry blackness.

Miss Evans called sharply, "Shirley!"

As she spoke, she stepped from one seat of the boat to the next. Perhaps because she was thinking of Shirley, perhaps because the boat lurched, she lost her footing, and slipped between the seats. She fell in a heap, her right foot doubling under her.

Shirley was in the boat in an instant.

Miss Evans, trying to rise, fell back with a moan.

"My foot," she murmured, "I guess I've — " She fainted in Shirley's arms.

Shirley knew what to do, because her mother sometimes fainted. With Dee's help, she laid Miss Evans as
flat as possible in the stern of the boat and sprinkled water
on her face. The counselor came to for a moment, opened
her eyes, and shut them again with a little moan.

"What'll we do, Shirley?" begged the twins.

Shirley thought fast. She looked across the water,
where the camp flag, a speck of color in the distance,
was fluttering down, ahead of the storm. On the other
horizon lightning was playing almost constantly, in the
angriest sky she had ever seen. Shirley measured the
storm against the distance home, and decided.

"Get in," she commanded the twins. "We've got to
get Miss Evans to a doctor."

There was a murmur from Miss Evans, as if in pro-
test, but Shirley paid no attention.

"You take the bow oars, Dee," she ordered, "and you
the number-three oars, Doris, and you number-two,

Dorothy. I'll stroke. We did it in fifteen minutes this morning, not half trying. Now we're going to row. Are you in? Get set — go!"

To Shirley the next fifteen minutes were timeless. Her steady, regular strokes gave confidence to the younger girls. But fast as they rowed, the storm came faster.

As Shirley rowed, she faced the storm. She watched the lightning get sharper, she heard it more closely followed by thunder, yet she was as unmoved as if it were all occurring on a moving picture screen. Her mind was concentrated on bringing her boat to shore.

Once Doris cried out at an unusually sharp flash which seemed to shatter the whole sweep of sky opposite them.

"Shut your eyes," called Shirley, firmly. "Pretend it's Crew Day and you're racing."

Shirley turned her head an instant to see how much farther they had to go. A third of the way yet! Could

the children do it? Would their strength hold out? Would it have been better to wait on the island, after all? At the same instant the question was answered.

Z-z-zz! A flash, so sharp it hissed, shot directly down into the island they had left. The clap was immediate and terrific. For a second, everybody was stunned. Doris gave a little yell, huddled in the bottom of the boat beside her twin, and lost an oar.

"Crawl up by Dorothy," Shirley shouted over her shoulder, "and help her pull. Here comes the rain."

Shirley pulled on and on.

"Heads down! Catch, pu-l-l! Catch, pu-l-l!" she gasped, acting as both cox and stroke.

Crash! Bang! Not so close this time!

Vaguely she was aware of another sound, but she pulled steadily on.

"Catch hold of this rope," called a voice. "We'll tow you in."

Shirley looked up.

Tom, the boathouse keeper, had come out in his small launch with Miss Allerton to meet them.

Five minutes later they were all safely ashore, and Miss Evans had been carried to the infirmary, where Miss Allerton and the camp nurse were applying first aid to her foot.

After supper that evening, Shirley sat with her campmates at Pow-wow waiting for the announcement of crews that must come tonight. Shirley wished that she were anywhere else in the world.

"You will all be glad to know," began Miss Allerton, "that the injury to Miss Evans's foot is a severe sprain, and not a break. Now we come to the business of this Pow-wow. I am sure that every one of you will agree with me that the most important position on a crew is that of stroke. It should go to a girl we have in camp who is fearless — "

Here Shirley hung her head.

" — capable of leading others, and of keeping her head in time of strain or danger. Therefore I have assigned the position of stroke on Crew A to — "

Miss Allerton's announcement was lost in the chant which rose from the whole group.

"Shirley Carlyle! Shirley Carlyle! Shirley Carlyle!"

After Pow-wow, Shirley sought Miss Allerton.

"May I tell Miss Evans?" she begged.

"Well, considering the location of the infirmary, I think it is possible she has heard already," Miss Allerton smiled. "But you may go if you'll stay just one minute."

Miss Evans greeted Shirley with a pale but happy little smile. Presently she said, "I could hear your voice over the thunder, going just like a cox's — 'Catch, pu-l-l! Catch, pu-l-l!' — and there wasn't a quiver in it."

"Why, Miss Evans!" Shirley cried in delight. "I hadn't thought about it before. There was a thunderstorm and I wasn't afraid!"

"I'm glad you weren't," replied Miss Evans. "I was."

Louise W. Bray

BY HOOK OR CROOK

Beaner's eyes were big with awe. "Boy, that was a good shot!" he said. "If only I had some marbles!"

"You'd beat me all hollow, wouldn't you?" laughed Jerry, his big brother.

"Oh, no, Jerry, no!" said Beaner. "You know I couldn't beat you — not for a long time. You're the champion!"

"I'm not champion yet," answered Jerry, but his eyes lit up. Champ! That's what he'd be tomorrow if he beat Dave Arnold in the finals of the marbles tournament of the Millbrook Public Schools. Champ! He fingered his precious shooter lovingly. He and the shooter together — they were going places tomorrow! He knew it!

With his shoe he slowly rubbed out the practice ring he had drawn on the ground and picked up his marbles. He counted them carefully before he drew tight the strings of the little bag.

Beaner was still talking earnestly. "If I had some marbles, I could practice every day while I'm at camp," he was saying, "I could be good too — if I just had some marbles!"

Jerry looked at his little brother's eager face. "I'll tell you what," he said. "There's a bag of my old marbles in my dresser drawer. You can put that in your suitcase when you pack tonight."

"Honest? For my very own?" Beaner shouted.

"For your very own," Jerry promised.

Beaner gave him a bear-hug. "Jerry, you're just the best ever!" he cried. "Do you know what I'm going to do? Tomorrow afternoon at two, when I know the match has started, I'm going to cross my fingers and wish for you to win!"

Jerry laughed and gave him a push. "Go along with you! Tomorrow at two you'll be so busy having fun at camp you'll have forgotten all about me!"

Jerry knew the fun of camp, for he had spent last summer there. This year it was Beaner's turn to go to camp, and Jerry had put his mind on something else, the school marbles tournament. If he won that, he would win, also, a chance to go to the state marbles tournament later in the summer.

Full of dreams, Jerry put his bag of marbles away and strolled over to the school grounds for a last look at tomorrow's arena.

The finals would be fought out in the game of oval ringtaw. Instead of shooting at a long line of commies from any position round a ring, the player must aim at a line of only three marbles from the end of an oval.

Jerry wandered around the school yard until dark, and then went home to sleep until the great day.

"Jerry! Jerry! Aren't you coming to the train with me?" It was Beaner pounding on his bedroom door that finally wakened Jerry from dreams of triumph. He sat up, rubbing his sleepy eyes and blinking at the morning light.

"Sure, I'm coming, Beaner!" he shouted.

"Please hurry, Jerry," his little brother begged. "We have to leave in fifteen minutes."

Fifteen minutes! "Whew!" Jerry whistled. He had overslept. Quickly he hurried into his clothes and joined an excited Beaner in the family sedan.

"Jerry, are you sure I'll like camp?" Beaner asked. "What will the other boys be like? Will I get homesick?"

Jerry answered these and other questions, one after another. Yes, he'd write to Beaner; no, he wouldn't forget to feed Beaner's pup; yes, he'd drive over with the family on Sundays to visit him. Camp wasn't far away, really.

When they reached the station the train was already in and Beaner nearly fell out of the car in his fear that it would go without him. Not until he was safely on the steps of the train did he remember what the day held for Jerry.

"Jerry," he cried then, "be sure to win!"

"Of course!" Jerry laughed. "I'll win by hook or by crook!" he promised.

Beaner looked happier. "I packed the marbles you gave me," he said. "Thanks ever so much, Jerry. I'm going to be almost as good a player as you are when I get back!"

"See that you are!" Jerry ordered sternly. Then, as the train steamed out of Millbrook, he grinned and waved his hand.

Jerry forced himself to eat his dinner, and even to lie down awhile on the porch swing. But when his mother called out, "Half past one, Jerry!" he was up like a flash.

He tore upstairs to get his precious bag of marbles. Let's see, he'd put it in this drawer. No, in this. But where was it? He pulled out socks and ties and all kinds of odds and ends, but no bag of marbles.

Anxiously he felt once more round the back of the drawer and touched something. He drew it out and gave a sigh of relief. He had his marbles! Then he sat down in dismay on the edge of his bed. This bag held nothing but chipped glassy relics of long-ago games!

"Beaner!" Jerry groaned, for now he knew that his little brother must have gone off to camp with the wrong bag of marbles. Beaner, who wouldn't have hurt his chances for anything in the world!

Jerry sat stunned. He'd have to forfeit the game to Dave.

Poor old Beaner! When he found he had taken Jerry's best marbles, when he heard Jerry had lost and knew he'd been the cause of it, the poor kid would be wild!

Jerry remembered his own promise to Beaner at the station. By hook or by crook he would win, he had said. Well, maybe he wouldn't give up the game without a struggle, after all. At least he could try!

On his way to the school yard, he sorted out the contents of the bag. There was only one marble that was even possible as a shooter, and even that big glassy had a chip out of it.

He tried it a few times, sending it ahead of him down the sidewalk. It had a decided roll to the left. How could he win a marble game with a shooter that hooked like that?

Hooked! Suddenly Jerry grinned. "By hook or crook," he had said to Beaner. Well, then, that's the way he would win! With an air of grave determination he drew a practice oval in the dirt a block from the school and knelt at the end of it.

The Tournament

The final game of the tournament was about to start when a small, tear-stained boy came panting down the street, followed by a young man. The boy pushed his way through the ring of boys around the two contestants and worked his way to the inside of the ring. There was Jerry and there was Dave, both looking strained and serious as they crouched back of the playing line.

"The games are two-up," the referee was announcing. "This one is the final. Dave will shoot first."

"Jerry!" the little boy cried. But the word was lost in the big shout that rose at that moment. Dave's shooter had spun into the oval and knocked the first of the three marbles almost out of the ring, leaving his own shooter inside the oval. The shouts increased as everyone offered advice.

"Hit his taw!" the crowd of boys urged. "Aim for his shooter! You can't leave him there!"

Jerry knelt behind the playing line, an anxious frown wrinkling his forehead. With so few commies up, every shot counted. If he wasted his turn in getting Dave out of position, Dave could just repeat his play next time, and Jerry would have to do it all over again. He could never win that way. But if Jerry should shoot and miss, leaving Dave in that beautiful position for his next shot — !

The sounds of advice died away in the crowd. The silence became tense. Even the little boy with tears running down his cheeks had stopped shouting, "Jerry!" and was watching, too.

Jerry took aim, and the little boy moaned. Why, he wasn't even aiming straight! He was shooting to the right. The old glass shooter was rolling into the oval for a complete miss.

Or was it? The little boy's eyes almost popped from his head. The crowd held its breath. Then there was a whoop as the shooter, without lessening speed, spun into a hook and knocked the second commie out of the oval.

"Score one for Jerry!" called the referee.

Jerry knelt for his next shot, this time at Dave's shooter. Again he took that odd aim to the right. Again his chipped old shooter curved in a long hook and rolled just past Dave's without touching it!

A long sigh swept through the crowd.

Jerry's shooter had gone out of the oval, so Dave aimed at the third commie, which was the only one left in its original position. Straight and true his shooter went, striking the commie cleanly, and carrying it out of the oval.

"One for Dave," the referee announced. "One-up in the final game!"

Dave's shooter had gone out of the oval on his last shot. He went back to the playing line. The remaining commie — the one he had almost knocked out on his very first shot — was at the farther end of the oval from him, but he had a clear shot at it.

It would take only a soft push to shove the commie over the line. Carefully he aimed. Straight as an arrow, the shooter rolled toward it, more and more slowly.

Jerry went limp. Dave's shooter had stopped just short of the commie!

New excitement rippled through the crowd of boys as they saw what the situation was. Dave's shooter was directly in Jerry's path! Jerry was stymied!

Even the audience had no advice to offer now. If Jerry should fail to knock Dave's shooter out of position, Dave had a set-up shot to win the game. But Jerry did not even look at Dave's shooter. He paced off the distance to the last commie, and studied it from all angles.

"Jerry, you're stymied!" the boys roared. "Take out his shooter! It's your only chance!"

Jerry paid no attention to their advice. Back at the playing line again, he knelt slowly. Then he shifted a little to the right. He rubbed his fingers against his trouser leg and took aim. Out into the oval spun the glass shooter. It rolled straight ahead, straight past Dave's shooter, straight past — not quite past the commie! At the last possible second, it swung into its crazy hook, curved to the left, and tapped the last commie gently over the line.

Bedlam broke loose. Jerry was surrounded by cheering boys. They pounded him and shook his hand and thumped him on the back. "The Champ!" they shouted.

Jerry tried to push through them. But someone was pulling him back. He looked around.

"Beaner!" he yelled.

Beaner lifted his tear-stained face. "I brought 'em back, Jerry," he cried. "As soon as I unpacked and found your marbles, I told the Director. He sent me back with a counselor. But I got here too late, Jerry."

Too late? Jerry thought of that last shot where his precious flint would have been useless.

"Beaner, you weren't a minute late," said Jerry. "And anyway, you shouldn't have worried. I told you I'd win, didn't I — by hook or by crook?"

Nan Gilbert

WHITEY'S FIRST ROUNDUP

WHITEY was eleven years old or thereabouts. He had a hand-me-down Stetson hat with a rattlesnake skin hatband and a pair of fancy-stitched, high-heeled boots, but even with all these trappings he was no great shakes for size.

Nevertheless, he considered himself practically a full-fledged cowboy after he had been living with his Uncle Torwal on the ranch for several years. He had practiced until he could walk almost as bow-legged as any cowboy.

"Reckon you'll be wanting me to go along on the roundup tomorrow, won't you, Uncle Torwal?" he said one day.

"What makes you reckon such a thing as that?" Uncle Torwal wanted to know.

"Well," said Whitey, "I'm just about top hand, I figure."

"Well, you'd better figure again," Uncle Torwal grinned. "Chances are the first day out you'd get us into some kind of a jam it would take us a week to get out of."

"No, I wouldn't, Uncle Torwal!" said Whitey. "Honest, I'd be mighty careful to mind just what you told me so I wouldn't be any trouble at all."

His uncle thought it over for a while. "Well, I reckon you've got to start some time," he said doubtfully. "Get your bed roll ready to go. But mind, the first bobble you make I'm a-going to send you back!"

"I won't make any bobble," Whitey promised him and tore off to find a tarpaulin to roll his bed in.

Long before sunup next morning everyone on the ranch was up and stirring. The cowboys rolled their roundup beds and threw them on the cook wagon after breakfast and went on to the corrals to catch up their horses.

Whitey was walking importantly over to throw his roll on the wagon with the others when Uncle Torwal stopped him. "What you got in there?" he asked.

"Just my bed," Whitey told him.

"Looks mighty big to me," his uncle grunted. "Unroll it and let me look at it."

Whitey untied the rope and rolled the canvas out. Inside he had seven blankets such as cowboys call sugans, two horse blankets, a feather pillow, and a piece of carpet.

"Listen, Old-timer, four sugans is enough for any cowhand. Take out the rest and leave them."

"Yes, sir!" Whitey said, and did as he was told. After he had taken care of that, he hurried around to the calf pasture to catch up old Spot.

Any other morning Spot would have been waiting at the pasture gate, ready for the bridle, but this morning he had other ideas. He capered around and snorted and refused to be caught. Whitey grew madder and madder. Finally he went back to the stable to see if maybe his uncle would help him.

"If you're going to be a cowhand, you'll have to catch your own horse," Uncle Torwal said. "Get a pan of oats and coax him up with that. If the other fellows are gone when you are ready, come on over to the old stage crossing on Hay Creek. That's where the first camp will be. It isn't ten miles and you know where the old road goes. But don't go taking any short cuts, now. You follow around by the road."

"Yes, sir," Whitey told him, and went for a pan of oats. He held his rope behind him while he shook the oat pan. Spot came trotting up, but he still was not ready to be caught. He would monkey around until he could reach out and get a mouthful of oats, then he would whirl and gallop off across the pasture.

Whitey saw the riders go out to start their day's circle. Later Catfish Smith, the roundup cook, climbed up on the high spring seat of the chuck wagon and drove off with his four-horse team. The horse wrangler with the bunch of extra saddle horses that cowboys call the remuda, followed along behind. And still Whitey had not caught his horse!

It wasn't until he was mad clear through, and everybody else was long gone, that Spot got tired of the game and let himself be caught. Whitey saddled up and pulled the cinch extra tight just for spite, and started out alone.

Once actually on the way to the roundup, however, Whitey felt better. He began to think that there was really no reason why he should go around by the road, in spite of what his uncle had said. He was pretty late already. Besides, he was practically a cowboy, wasn't he? And cowboys didn't go around by the roads when they wanted to go places. They went across country. So he went that way.

After he had ridden a few miles, he came on an old buffalo wallow. Often there are Indian arrowheads to be found in such places. Whitey got off to take a look. After a few minutes' searching had convinced him there were none here, he decided he had better be on his way. But when he looked around for Spot, Spot was gone!

Whitey had been riding with his bridle reins tied together. When he got off he had forgotten to throw them over Spot's head and drop them on the ground. Now a Western horse is trained to stand and wait if the reins are dropped on the ground, but if they are left over his neck, he will go away and leave his rider behind.

Here was a pickle, for sure. Spot would go back to the ranch, Whitey knew. There was nothing for him to do but to walk back too. He hitched up his belt and started walking. From the top of the next rise he saw Spot just going out of sight over the next ridge, half a mile away.

After that Whitey was alone in the middle of the prairie. He tramped along, madder than a hornet, and tried to remember some of the terrible things he had heard Catfish Smith mutter to his horses. Here it was his first day on the roundup and already he had let himself be set afoot like any greenhorn.

Then his feet started to hurt. His high-heeled boots were fine for riding, but they were never made to walk in. Before he had gone a mile he had blisters on both heels. And home was a long way off.

As if his feet were not trouble enough, Whitey, when he limped up over a little knoll, came face to face with a bunch of range cattle. So now, besides being mad and footsore, he was scared. For he knew that wild cattle will not bother a man on a horse, but he did not know what they would do to one on foot.

There were no trees to climb, nor any fences to get behind, so he stood still and wondered what in the world he should do.

The cattle threw up their heads when they saw him, and started edging toward him. He did not dare run. When he tried to yell at them, he found that for some reason he could not make a sound. They came up and stood in a circle watching him and he watched them. Now and again, one of them would give a low bellow and paw dirt into the air. Whitey would have gladly given his Stetson hat with the rattlesnake hatband and his fancy-stitched boots to have been somewhere else.

Just when he had about given up hope of ever getting

home again, he saw Uncle Torwal riding his way, leading Spot. Uncle Torwal shouted and waved his hat and the cattle moved off.

"Find the walking kind of crowded?" Uncle Torwal asked him, grinning.

"Yes, just a mite," Whitey said, hoping he did not look as scared as he felt.

"If you had just yelled and waved your hat, they'd have gone away. But your standing still made them curious about you."

"They looked mean," Whitey said as he climbed into the saddle.

Uncle Torwal did not say anything more as they rode on toward camp. Whitey knew he had made a bobble, but there did not seem to be much that he could do about it. Acting like a greenhorn twice on the day of his first roundup was pretty bad.

When the pair came in sight of the chuck wagon, there was already a big herd of cattle gathered on the flats near by. The cowboys were eating their dinner, squatting on the ground around Catfish Smith's Dutch ovens.

When they had eaten, Whitey expected to be sent back, but, instead, his uncle set him to dragging up wood for the cook fire and the branding fire. He gathered dry limbs from the cottonwood trees near by and dragged them up on the end of a rope from his saddle horn.

When he had gathered enough for both fires he sat on his horse and watched the branding. A cowboy would ride into the herd and, after some maneuvering, would flip

his noose around a calf's legs, and drag him out to the branding fire, with the mother following anxiously.

"Quarter Circle Z!" the cowboy would sing out, or "Triangle T," or "Turkey Track," depending on what brand the old cow wore. While Uncle Torwal took the proper branding iron out of the fire, Birdlegs Johnson and another cowboy grabbed the calf and stretched it on the ground. Uncle Torwal would slap the hot iron on the calf's side, the calf would bellow, more surprised than hurt, and a few minutes later would be up and tearing across the flat.

Whitey was sitting there watching, swinging the loop in his rope, when Uncle Torwal slapped the iron onto a calf that let out a bellow you could hear half a mile. At that his mother rushed out of the herd with her head down and her tail straight up. It was plain to see that she was aiming for the men on the ground around the fire.

Now it is not hard to dodge a bull, because he shuts his eyes and charges blind. But an old cow does not make that mistake. So Uncle Torwal and the men were trying to get out of there quick. Except for Whitey, there did not happen to be anyone on a horse near enough to stop her.

To get to the fire, she had to pass Whitey and Spot. When Whitey looked back and saw her, he swung his loop at her to head her off and quite by accident caught her head in the noose. Spot was half asleep, but when the rope went past his head he remembered his cowhorse days and braced himself. The cow hit the end of the rope with a crash and turned head over heels, landing on her side almost in the branding fire. By the time she gathered her wits, more men had ridden up to drive her off.

After the excitement was over, Uncle Torwal said to Whitey, "Reckon that makes us even now, cowboy. If you haven't anything else to do, you can tend the branding fire and keep tally for me."

"Yes, sir!" said Whitey. "That'd suit me just fine!"

Glen Rounds

CHRISTMAS PRESENT RACE

THE December wind whistled around the point of land called Blind Man's Beat. The small, old-fashioned ice-boat tipped at a dangerous angle, but Judy Barton shifted her weight to windward to bring the light side down again. Jeff, her twin brother, held onto the tiller, his face wrinkled against the driving wind.

"Ready about!" ordered Jeff. Then, as Judy ducked her head, he began to turn the little boat sharply around the point of the Beat.

"Hard alee!" He snapped out the final command and the little *Frost* glided smoothly before the wind on the black ice to the south of the Beat.

Judy took one look at the green and red sails in front of them. Then she looked back at her brother and shook her head.

"We gained some," she said, "but not enough to take us into the finals."

Jeff said nothing but blew on one frosty hand while he guided his boat with the other. You couldn't expect even the best seamanship to make up the difference between an old crate like the *Frost* and the trim and shining new ice-boats ahead of them. Still, Jeff had hoped that their choice of a tack around Blind Man's Beat would help. Now he watched the boats ahead glide into the dock of the Shrewsbury Boat Club. Their sails rattled as their owners

brought them up into the wind. A moment later the sails began to come down.

"I guess the *Snow Queen* and the *Icicle* and the *North Wind* will be the cup defenders," Judy said, naming the first three boats.

Jeff nodded. "Well, that's fair enough," he said. "But I just wish — "

Judy nodded and the wish hung between them, the stronger for being unspoken. They both wished with all their hearts that they could have managed to take part in the coming races on the river between the Shrewsbury Boat Club and the Pine Point Club farther up.

"We wouldn't have been so bad in the finals," Judy said, as they swung into the harbor. "The course takes knowing the river as much as anything."

"Well, we won't have the chance," Jeff said grimly.

The following week Jeff and Judy almost forgot about the ice-boating because it was the week before Christmas. There were Christmas presents to get ready and to deliver,

including the carved wooden box they had made for Miss Mary Scarborough.

Miss Mary was a special friend of the twins. They had first come to know her one summer when their catboat had stuck in the marsh near her lonely old house on the Knoll, at the end of Blind Man's Beat. Jeff and Judy had gone ashore for help and had run into the sharptongued, erect old lady who lived alone on the Beat with her housekeeper and an old Scotch gardener.

The gardener had helped them launch the boat and they had sailed away. But the next day, with more skillful handling of their boat, they had managed to put in at Miss Mary's old dock and had gone ashore to thank her.

From then on, they had been friends. Once or twice Miss Mary had invited them to a picnic on her point. Another time they had asked her to sail with them in their catboat. Miss Mary had not accepted their invitation but she seemed pleased to be asked.

When Christmastime came, they began to wonder how they could get Miss Mary's Christmas present to her.

"Maybe Mother'll take us in the car," Judy said.

When they suggested this, Mother shook her head. "I'm afraid there isn't a chance," she said, looking out of the window. "The road down Blind Man's Beat is so icy it cannot be used. Jim Andrews told me so this morning down at the store."

The twins went upstairs to Jeff's room to talk the matter over.

"We might wait," Judy suggested. "There is one more day before Christmas. Maybe tomorrow Mother could get across."

"That's her busiest day of the year," Jeff said. "We can't ask her to do it then."

Judy and Jeff moved over to the window and stared out over the frozen surface of the Shrewsbury River.

"We've just got to take the present ourselves," Jeff said suddenly. "And we'd better take it today."

"In case there's a thaw," Judy finished his thought for him. "We'll go right now in the *Frost*."

CHRISTMAS PRESENTS

They pulled on their warmest clothes then and there and walked down to the ice-boat house. The place was deserted except for old Ben Burton, who had charge of the boats.

"It's nasty sailing," Ben warned them, when he had helped get the *Frost* off the wooden blocks and onto the ice. "The river's as uneven as a new-plowed field."

As soon as they had their sails up and Jeff had given

a push-off, they understood what he meant. It certainly was nasty sailing. The wind was fitful and tricky. In some places it had piled up little waves which had frozen into ridges of ice. In other places there was a short fair space of black ice which was edged with a white scum that looked treacherous.

"I think we'll go as close to the Knoll as we can," Jeff said.

Judy huddled down on the flat spruce bottom of the *Frost*. The Knoll was on the south side of the Beat. If they couldn't reach Miss Mary that way there was no other point of approach except along the marshes which bounded the Beat on the north, and the marshes were almost always impossible to cross.

It was a long, cold sail — longer and colder than any Judy remembered. The wind was dead against them so that they were continuously going about for one short tack after another.

"We'll just fly going home," Judy said, but Jeff wasn't sure. He squinted up at the bleak sky and shrugged his shoulders. The wind was coming due north right now, but it looked shifty. That was just the trouble with a day like this.

They were nearly at the Knoll before Jeff enjoyed his trip at all. Then he began to relax as much as he could in that dull, cramping cold. He looked up at his sail. It was well filled with wind, and Jeff started to whistle. Just that second Judy let out a shout.

"Open water!" she yelled.

For one dreadful instant Jeff was struck dumb. The next instant he shouted, "Hard alee!" Then he put his tiller over with all his strength.

There was a flap of the sail, the hiss of runners cutting the ice. The next instant the *Frost* slid forward on still another tack. Jeff hunched down to look under the sail and to see where Judy was pointing. There was open water all right — yards and yards of it, black and wind-rippled.

"That was close!" said Jeff.

Judy turned to look at him.

"Close!" she said. Her clear blue eyes were frightened. "That gap stretches all the way from the Knoll right to the south side of the Beat. We can't go on this way. Not possibly."

Jeff measured the distance between himself and the dark curving outline of Blind Man's Beat and it seemed to grow longer every time he looked at it.

"There's still the marsh," he said. "That must be flooded after all the rain we've had lately, and it's on the north. Do you want to try it?"

For the first time that afternoon Judy grinned. "What do you think?" she said. "Do you think I want to go home?"

Jeff grunted approval and once more barked the orders. "Ready about. Hard alee!"

They made the distance to the north side of Blind Man's Beat in fairly good time and then they saw the marshes in front of them. Most of the short stubble reeds that

might trip them were covered with good ice, but here and there a clump of brown stalks stood up like an Indian's topknot.

"It'll take sailing," Judy warned, peering under the sail. "You've got to give those clumps a wide berth."

Jeff did not stop to talk. He took his sight from the end of Blind Man's Beat and began sailing straight forward. Once he had to go about to escape a clump of reeds and another time the ice creaked beneath them. Still the *Frost* moved steadily ahead.

They were nearly over the marsh when Judy saw a last fringe of stiff stubble between them and the clear ice near the shore.

"Jeff, look!" Judy warned.

They drew near the fringe, nearer and nearer. There was no gap in it, no way of skirting it.

"Hold tight!" Jeff roared. Even as he spoke, they went over it safely. The ice was still thin. It groaned and creaked beneath them but Jeff no longer cared. They were near shore. They were very near shore. A few short tacks and they were alongside Miss Mary Scarborough's boathouse.

When they finally had the sails down and had stepped on shore Jeff's knees shook and Judy was so cold that her lips were blue. Finally she untied the red-wrapped package from the *Frost's* center rail where they had fastened it and followed Jeff onto the uneven beach.

"Well," she said, "that was something. It's going to be even trickier going home."

"We can do it," Jeff said shortly, and led the way up to Miss Mary's big, lonely house.

Miss Mary was even happier to see them than they had expected. She led them into her sitting room and put them close beside the cozy welcoming fire while she went out to order some cocoa.

When the old housekeeper brought in the steaming, fragrant cups on a tray, there were two small packages lying beside them.

"For you," Miss Mary said. "Open them now. I like to open packages before Christmas. Don't you?"

Jeff grinned and opened his package while Miss Mary and Judy opened theirs.

"Boy!" Jeff almost shouted, when the last piece of tissue paper was pulled away. "A compass! What a beauty!"

He looked at Judy and saw that her gift was a stop watch, a really good stop watch, like the one Mr. Harris used to start the boat races. Jeff looked back at his compass and clicked down the lid with a little snap.

"Boy!" he said again. "These are wonderful!"

"I'm glad you like them," said Miss Mary. "They're not nearly so nice as my box, but I thought they might be useful in your next races."

Jeff nodded, but as he pocketed his compass a chilly feeling of disappointment shot through him. He and Judy wouldn't have any more races — at least, not until the following summer when they took out the catboat. As far as the ice-boat race was concerned, they were out.

They pulled on their mittens, waved to Miss Mary,

133

and hurried down to the boathouse. The *Frost* was just where they had left her, looking as old and forlorn as a battered scarecrow.

As Jeff began to pull up the sail, he felt the new strength of the wind. "The wind's changed," he said. "It's going to be even more exciting going home."

It was exciting, but at least the excitement came at the beginning of the run. They headed for the marsh once, and then, as the wind failed, Jeff brought the *Frost* about.

"We've got to wait for a real puff," he said slowly. "And if it gives out just when we're halfway over, we're in trouble."

Judy edged her way toward the tiller, her eyes still ahead of her, searching for the best ice. Finally there was a sharp puff of wind.

"All set?" Jeff asked.

Judy nodded, at the same time that her hand was moving toward the cleat.

The puff carried them safely over the flooded, frozen marsh and onto the black ice on the far side.

"Boy!" breathed Judy, as they slid smoothly over the good ice. "We made it in quick time."

Jeff said nothing, but headed the *Frost* down the long frozen channel toward the boathouse. Now the wind was with them. If only it did not shift, they would soon be home.

The wind stayed favorable and in a few minutes it brought them within sight of the boathouse. Ben Burton had lighted a fire on the shore. They could see his figure and another, moving beside the leaping red flames.

"Home free!" Judy said as they slid over the rough ice of the harbor. "Home free and nobody took an ice bath."

Jeff nodded, one hand on his tiller and one hand on his pocket, where he could feel the bulge of the compass. He turned the *Frost* skillfully windward and in another moment they had the sail down and were taking it off.

By the time Ben had started to help them lift the *Frost* up on the blocks, the twins saw that Mr. Harris, the president of the Boat Club, was the other figure beside the fire.

"Well," he said, as they moved nearer the good warmth, "you twins go out on any sort of ice. How far did you get?"

"Up to Blind Man's Beat," Jeff said quietly. Then Judy told him how they had nearly ended up in the open water on the south side.

"How did you finally manage?" Mr. Harris asked. His face, in the red firelight, was full of interest.

"Over the marsh," Judy told him. "Jeff knew it would be flooded, and we were pretty sure it would be frozen."

For a moment Mr. Harris did not say anything. At last he muttered, "Well!" and led the way inside the warm, dry boathouse. "You young people know your river," he said then. "How would you like to sail in the Pine Point race?"

For once Jeff spoke before Judy. "Like it?" he said. "We'd like it better than anything else in the world, but — " he hesitated, and then blurted out honestly, "the *Frost* came in last in the trial race, you know."

Mr. Harris nodded and dismissed their boat with one shrug of his broad shoulders. "I wasn't talking about the *Frost*," he said. "I meant, how would you like to sail my *Snow Queen?* I'm looking for a pair who know the river."

"It'd be just about the nicest thing that ever happened," breathed Judy. Jeff said nothing, but Mr. Harris could read the look on his face.

A few minutes later, the twins marched up the hill toward home.

"Aren't we lucky!" said Jeff, as they sighted the yellow lights of their own house. "A compass and a stop watch and the chance to sail the best ice-boat on the river!"

"Not to mention crossing the marsh without a crack-up," laughed Judy. "Aren't you glad we decided to take Miss Mary her Christmas present?"

Lavinia Davis

SPEED WAYS

A LOCOMOTIVE

In the daytime, what am I?
In the hubbub, what am I?
A mass of iron and of steel,
Of boiler, piston, throttle, wheel,
A monster smoking up the sky,
  A locomotive!
    That am I!

In the darkness, what am I?
In the stillness, what am I?
Streak of light across the sky,
A clanging bell, a shriek, a cry,
A fiery demon rushing by,
  A locomotive
    That am I!

Lucy Sprague Mitchell

SKY HIGH

At times my world is wet and dull
(I am a Navy seaplane's hull)
But now I feel the water lash
Against my skin; and now the dash
Along the bay — a buoyant run —
Is over and I feel the sun.
And friendly wind and know the sky
Is all around. I'm quickly dry;
While by my side on hurtling wings
Are sister ships; they're graceful things.
We're strung on heaven's vast lagoon,
A roaring necklace for the moon.
To Navy men the thrill is trite —
It's just another routine flight;
But down within my metal keel
I know a thrill they'll never feel.
Just think: I am a simple boat,
And yet — upon the air I float!

R. H. Wade

THE KAYAK

Over the briny wave I go,
In spite of the weather, in spite of the snow;
What cares the hardy Eskimo?
In my little skiff with paddle and lance,
I glide where the foaming billows dance.
Round me the birds slip and soar;
Like me, they love the ocean's roar.

Sometimes a floating iceberg gleams
Above me with its melting streams;
Sometimes a rushing wave will fall
Down on my skiff and cover it all.
But what care I for a wave's attack?
With my paddle I right my little kayak,
And then its weight I speedily trim,
And over the water away I skim.

Unknown

141

OUTBOARD MOTOR

SLIPPING the land-detaining tether,
Suddenly we are off together,
My boat and I beneath the sky;
A sharp wind blowing, and the cry
Of wild geese down the windy way;
A stinging lash of silver spray
Cutting my face, my eyes, my hair;
A wild, exhilarating air,
And the mad water everywhere.
My boat, an arrow whose bright speed
Is like a racer in the lead,
Is like a winging bird set free,
Is like a broncho under me.
It splits the waves, it lifts until
It climbs a high green water hill,
And rushes on, while in its wake
Is churning foam and waves that break
Like surf upon some rocky shore,
Its sound lost in the motor's roar.
I am a part, this heady hour
Of all earth's motion, light, and power.

Grace Noll Crowell

WORKING AND WINNING

CORN-BELT BILLY

"GOOD-BY, Corn-Belt Billy."

Billy was too surprised by this unexpected name to answer. He managed a half-hearted wave of the hand as the automobile moved slowly out of the farmyard. Keith, the tourist boy, leaned from the car window, his grin friendly, but mocking. As the car gained the highway and disappeared, Billy walked toward the barn. On his face was a thoughtful scowl. "Corn-Belt Billy" indeed!

He remembered his conversation last night with Keith, though the latter had done most of the talking. He had been eager to tell Billy of his travels. Keith and his father and mother were returning to their home in New Hampshire after a tour of the West. Last evening, weary and hot, they had stopped at the white farmhouse where Billy lived. It seemed like a cool haven of peace in the long green shadows of evening, with its hospitable sign at the gate, "Tourists Welcome."

While Keith's parents rested on the pleasant porch chatting with Billy's mother, the two boys went off by themselves. They sat on the hay in the wide-open door of the barn loft and told each other their names, their grades at school, and other important bits of information. Before them stretched the acres of corn lands that belonged to Billy's widowed mother. Beyond the corn was a bit of thick woodland, a wide field of shocked wheat, pasture land, and a row of willows along the creek.

"You have a lot of corn, haven't you?" Keith said.

"Sure," said Billy. The blades of the young corn glistened like silver in the evening light. From the loft one could see how the plants marched in orderly rows, like green-clad soldiers, until they stopped at the far boundary fence, half a mile away to the left. Jed, the hired man, thought there would be a bumper crop this year, "providing there's no chinch bugs, ear worms, corn borers, smut, or rot," he had said, with a grin.

Keith knew nothing of such things. He was not a farmer boy. "You haven't much scenery here in the Middle West, though," he went on. "It's flat. Corn belt — that's what they call it. Nothing but corn."

"Oh, I don't know," objected Billy mildly. "There's a lot of wheat and barley and oats and timothy and clover. And there are rivers and creeks and woods and hollows."

"I see you haven't been around much," answered Keith, rather loftily. "We have scenery in New Hampshire. People come from everywhere to see it. And oh, boy! You ought to see the Far West! That's all scenery."

Keith had then launched into an enthusiastic description of his travels, illustrating his story with snapshots of which he had reason to be proud. Billy, used to the flat prairie country, pored over the pictures of the Rockies, gaunt and jagged and mighty. The words stumbled over one another in Keith's eager effort to describe the color and immensity of the Grand Canyon, and to explain how his donkey had picked its careful way down Bright Angel Trail. He told of the desert, and Billy seemed to see the tourists' automobile, a tiny black ant on the highway that stretched like an endless ribbon across the sands. There were pictures, too, of sand lying in ripples like the ripples of water, or curled in sculptured drifts.

Billy heard about California and the giant redwoods. He heard about Oregon and Washington, with their mighty mountains in the Cascade Range, their thick forests, their rivers and waterfalls and picturesque bays. He saw, sometimes in a snapshot and sometimes in his mind's eye, the plumes of steam from hot pools in Yellowstone Park, boiling caldrons of mud, and tall white geysers of water jetting into the air at exact intervals. He laughed over Keith's swim in Salt Lake, where the sands were of salt, and the gulls were like those that dip into the foam and spray of coastal seas. It had been surprising to the eastern boy to see them so far inland.

146

"No," Keith had ended his story rather abruptly, as his mother called him to bed, "you haven't any scenery round here. It's just corn belt."

Billy had often heard his mother's tourist-guests telling on summer evenings the story of their travels. But it was different hearing the same stories from a boy his own age. As he listened, Billy felt for the first time in his life a real longing for other places. Bright Angel Trail — the lovely name haunted him.

When Keith had said last night that the Midwest possessed no scenery, Billy had not particularly minded. Perhaps it was true. He scanned the landscape with a critical eye. But this morning! To be called "Corn-Belt Billy"!

"Makes me feel like a hick," he murmured, resentfully.

There was some final cultivating to be done in the cornfield that day. Billy, usually a willing worker, grumbled. "Nothing but corn — nothing but corn. I'm sick of the old stuff."

Jed tinkered with the tractor for a moment. "Just listen to the corn," he said, cocking one ear. "It's a-growing! You can hear it. There's nothing finer on this earth than a fine stand of corn like this here." He peered over the green blades at Billy. "You've got to like corn if you're going to be a farmer in these parts, kid."

"Maybe I won't be a farmer," answered Billy. His heart jumped at the surprise of his own rebellion. He felt almost wicked.

"Your mother would be right disappointed," declared Jed. "That she would. Working hard she is to keep this

147

farm going for you to take over some day. Your dad was a fine farmer before you. He'd a-wanted you to be a farmer, too. By gum!" Jed glared fiercely at Billy. "What's come over you? You must've eaten something."

Helping his mother to gather beans that evening, Billy saw her straighten her tired back. He saw her shade her eyes with her hand, looking over at the cornfields.

"There's beauty in corn, too, son," she said quietly.

Funny how a mother always knew what was in a lad's mind. She must have heard those farewell words of

Keith's. Somehow she knew what bitter seeds they had sown.

"Mountains must be very beautiful," continued Mother. "I've never seen them, but I like the poems about them. But poets have written of corn, too. Maize, the Indians called it. You remember what Longfellow says:

> Till at length a small green feather
> From the earth shot slowly upward,
> Then another and another,
> And before the summer ended,
> Stood the maize in all its beauty,
> With its shining robes about it,
> And its long, soft, yellow tresses;
> And in rapture, Hiawatha
> Cried aloud, "It is Mondamin!
> Yes, the friend of man, Mondamin!"

" 'The friend of man,' " repeated Mother, and turned smiling to Billy. He flushed and turned away, embarrassed at the sound of poetry from the lips of a farmer woman, surprised that she could quote it so freely. Billy liked to hear his teacher reading those measured phrases at school about Hiawatha, wrestling with Mondamin in the forest, slaying him that he might rise again as maize to feed the people. But to link the legend with these familiar corn lands, well, wasn't that all foolishness? "The friend of man." Billy had been feeling all day that the corn, on the contrary, was his enemy, making him a fellow that could be laughed at and called "Corn-Belt Billy."

149

A week or two later Mother's cousin, John Sutherland, came and stopped overnight. He was an extension worker on the staff of the big agricultural college in the northern part of the state. He was beginning an investigation tour of the corn belt. Billy had a great surprise when his mother told him at breakfast the next morning that he could go with Cousin John if he liked.

"Hurray!" cried Billy. "I'm going to travel!"

His mother washed and ironed all morning and packed his clean clothes in the old suitcase that had not been used for a long time. After dinner they were off. They would be gone for four weeks, traveling through the rest of Indiana, Illinois, Iowa, Missouri, perhaps part of Kansas and Nebraska.

Every morning during the tour, Billy arose, flushed and excited with the importance of travel. It never occurred to him that the country through which they rode was very similar to his own homeland. There were hundreds of miles of almost-level prairie, hundreds of cornfields. There were hundreds of farmyards and pastures filled with hundreds of cattle feeding on hundreds of bushels of corn, all fattening for the market, just as at home.

In Illinois the black soil lay deep and fertile. In Iowa the fields promised a harvest rich enough to feed an entire hungry world. Missouri and Kansas were burdened with growing grain. All were a part of the "bread basket of the world," as Cousin John expressed it.

Cousin John talked with many farmers, in grange meetings and on the farm. He examined the growing corn, stripping back the husks. Sometimes Billy saw his fingers covered with the smut that sickened and deformed the ears, and he would hear Cousin John tell the discouraged farmer of smut-resistant varieties. Sometimes the juicy kernels would be eaten by worms, or the tall stalks would be lying flat, destroyed by borers. Then he would hear talk of quarantine, of rotation of crops, of deeper cultivation. With Cousin John, Billy attended the meetings of boys' corn clubs. He met boys who had won trophies at fairs for the best corn — corn they had raised themselves.

"I'm a farmer, too," Billy would say, importantly, forgetting the treason he had expressed to Jed that day in the cornfield.

Cousin John took Billy to Chicago. "A little extra excursion," he called the trip. They went to a packing plant, the largest in the world. As they saw the long procession of live animals passing through the gate to slaughter, Cousin John said, "Corn on the hoof, Billy. Corn from the corn belt, transformed into meat."

They visited the Board of Trade Building. Billy saw the great tall-windowed room where corn was bought and sold. There the price was determined to the accompaniment of men's excited voices and the constant ticking of telegraph instruments.

They went to the docks of Lake Michigan, and saw

grain and meat from the corn belt being loaded into long freighters that traveled through the chain of lakes on their way to the sea.

Cousin John said that Billy ought to see how some of the by-products of corn were manufactured. Accordingly, they visited a starch factory, and saw not only the making of starch, but of gluten feed for cattle, of dextrin, of corn syrup, and of corn oil. Cousin John explained how these by-products also produced their own by-products. He told of many other important things that are made from corn.

"Denatured alcohol, Billy, for your mother's car in freezing weather. Cooking oils for her pies and cakes and salad dressings. The eraser on your pencil. The rubber soles on your shoes."

From Chicago Billy sent a post card to Keith.

"I am having a fine trip with my cousin," he wrote. "We haven't seen any mountains, but lots of other things. Mountains are important, but so is corn. If you ever come back I will tell you about it. So long."

He started to sign his name in the usual way, but impulsively he crossed out the first letters. "Corn-Belt Billy," he wrote with a flourish, and gazed at the signature with an amazing sense of personal triumph.

Turning homeward at last, Billy was suddenly eager to get there. What if smut or chinch bugs or borers had attacked his mother's beautiful field of corn — his corn!

They drove through the farmyard gate one late afternoon. It was home — quiet, familiar, prosperous, secure.

His mother's welcoming smile seemed beautiful to Billy. After greetings were over, Billy ran out to the cornfield. How the corn had grown! It was more than twice his height. The ears felt full and firm under the tight green husks. He climbed up on the fence and looked over the field. The plants marched along like tall, proud soldiers, waving green banners of victory, wearing golden plumes on their heads.

Suddenly Billy was reminded of his mother's words, "There's beauty in corn."

Exploring the cornfield, Billy found a monstrous ear. It was the longest he had ever seen. He hung his hat on it to mark its place in the field, and ran to the house. Mother and Cousin John and Jed came to see it.

"Why don't you exhibit it at the State Fair?" suggested Cousin John.

"What's the use?" grinned Jed. "Billy's not going to be a farmer."

"I am too," replied Billy, turning red.

"If that's the case," answered Jed, "I know something better you can do. Neighbor Wasson was telling me that they've put up a fine new stable at the State Fair grounds this summer. The Governor's going to dedicate it with the longest ear of corn in the state. There's your chance, kid."

The long ear of corn was plucked from its stalk to be sent away. It measured fourteen and seven-eighths inches in length. And on a certain afternoon in September, Billy and his mother stood by the Governor's side at the State

Fair, while crowds of people watched the ceremonies connected with the dedication of the stable. From the Governor's hand dangled a long white satin ribbon. At its other end hung a giant ear of corn.

"This ear of corn, the longest in the state," said the Governor, "was grown on the farm of Mrs. W. H. Russell, of English County. This boy, Billy Russell, is her son, who will some day inherit the farm."

Then the Governor broke the ear over the edge of the concrete dedication plate. He turned and placed in the

hands of Billy's mother the trophy, a beautiful silver cup. Then he shook hands with Billy.

"I hope you'll always grow corn like this, son," he said.

"Well, of course this isn't really my corn," answered Billy, frankly. "It's Mother's. Jed's, too. He's our hired man. But Mother says I can raise my own corn next year." He looked up at the Governor and grinned. "Once somebody called me 'Corn-Belt Billy,' and it made me mad as a hornet. But now I don't care if everybody calls me that!"

"Three cheers for Corn-Belt Billy!" shouted the Governor.

"Hurrah for Corn-Belt Billy!" shouted the crowd.

Mabel Leigh Hunt

MEALS FOR MICKEY

I T'S too hot to do anything like this," said Tim. He ran his hands through his wet, fair hair until it stood on end.

Tim and his sister Robin were peeling the wallpaper from the walls of his room. They lived in a small white house, snuggled close to the Connecticut hillside, a comfortable little house with a gray roof and climbing roses over the doorways. It had not belonged to the Storms long enough for them to be quite used to it; in fact, they had bought it only three months before. Inside the house there was still a great deal to be done. It was an old house and had not been lived in for years.

"Mother said this old wallpaper could wait a day or two until it was cooler," said Tim.

"I like to see the different layers underneath," said Robin. "They aren't the same all round the room."

"Maybe it was hot and the paper hanger got tired of peeling off paper — like us," said Tim. He looked out of the window at the little village that lay in the valley, far below their own house. A bright red roof stood out from among the gray ones.

"Look, Robin! That's the new hot-dog stand. Let's go down there and get a frozen custard. Have you a nickel? I have."

"Yes," said Robin, "but I was going to buy — "

"Oh, come on. It's too hot to do anything else. We'll stop and ask Mother if we may go."

A few minutes later Tim and Robin were on their way to the hot-dog stand. Under a large tree there were several tables. One was vacant.

"Let's eat out here," said Robin. They sat down and soon were eating the cold frozen custard.

"M-m! This is the stuff," said Tim. "Make it last a long time, Robin."

Robin took a quarter of a spoonful. Then she dropped her spoon in the dish and cried, "Tim, look! Look!"

An enormous tan-colored dog was coming through the doorway of the little house. Slowly it walked over to the table where the children sat. For a moment it stood looking at them, then came forward and stood beside Robin, wagging its tail.

157

"It's a Great Dane!" said Robin. She patted the huge head. "He's friendly."

The woman who kept the stand came out. "Don't you want a dog?" she asked.

Robin and Tim stared at her, wondering if they had heard the words correctly.

"A dog? You don't mean we may have this one!"

The woman nodded. "Yes. I haven't had him long. His master moved away and couldn't take him, and so he gave him to us. Since we've had the stand, he's been a great bother. He's scared of the motorcycles — shivers when he hears one. And he frightens the customers. Gentle as a kitten he is, but how would they ever know that?"

Robin looked at Tim. "Shall we go home and ask Mother first?"

"If we do," said Tim, "she'll say 'no.' But if we walk into the yard with a perfectly beautiful dog, she won't have the heart to refuse. Let's try it, anyway."

"You'll have no trouble holding him," said the woman, as she snapped the leash on the big dog's collar. "He's trained to walk beside you and not tug at the leash."

"What is his name?" asked Robin. Her answer made both children laugh and they were still giggling as they went up the road. They took turns holding the leash, and the big dog paced along with them like a dignified gentleman. They found Mother in the garden when they turned in the gate.

"Mother," said Tim, with a confidence he did not really feel, "this is our new dog."

158

"Well, really!" said Mother. "Nothing much surprises me any more, but this is a little difficult. Suppose you explain."

It took quite a bit of explaining. Mother looked doubtful. The children looked worried. Then the dog walked up to Mother and rubbed his head against her.

"He's pretty nice," admitted Mother. "What is his name?"

"Mickey Mouse!" said Robin in a slightly choked voice, and all three of them laughed until they ached.

"Mickey Mouse!" said Mother. "It simply can't be. I think I'll say you can keep him if you change his name. A Great Dane named Mickey Mouse is just too much."

"Hooray! We can keep him!" shouted Tim. "Mom, you're a good sport!"

"We could call him Sir Michael," said Robin. "Mickey for short."

"Of course, there's Father to be thought of, too," said Mother. "It's time to go to meet his train. Let's all go to the station and break the news."

Father took the news calmly but said just one thing that disturbed everyone.

"My dear young friends," he said, "have you remembered that your father is an artist and that sometimes he makes money and sometimes not? And have you thought of how much food a Great Dane eats in one day?"

"How much?" asked Robin anxiously.

"Four pounds of meat," answered Father.

There was dead silence. Everyone knew about the price

of meat. Since they had bought the house, there had not been much extra money.

"We'll have to do something to earn the money," said Tim desperately. "We'll have to keep him. Perhaps I could mow lawns."

"We'll think it over," said Father. "Remember you're not so good at mowing even our own lawn. Anyway, we'd better stop at the store and get the animal some food. We can't let him starve to death."

The Storms all sat around and watched Mickey eat his first meal, four pounds of it. It was all over in an astonishingly short time.

"If only his mouth were smaller, or something," said Robin. "It's like the Mammoth Cave of Kentucky."

"That wouldn't help. It's his stomach that's too big," said Tim. "I've read that if you don't eat for days your stomach shrinks. Maybe we could shrink his."

"Not a chance," said Father gloomily.

Night came and with it the question of a bed for Mickey. Mickey himself settled it, for he stretched out on the rug in front of the fire.

"He looks as if he'd always been here!" said Tim. "I guess dogs know when people really want them."

Next day the Storms began to find that having a Great Dane in a small house is like having an elephant in a space too small for him. They had to get used to Mickey, and even though he tried his best to be helpful about his size he was quite often in the way.

In the afternoon a friend of Mother's came to visit, a

friend who owned a very small Pomeranian called Ducky.
Tim and Robin called him the puff-ball, and did not consider him a dog at all. Somehow, when the puff-ball arrived, Mother forgot about Mickey. Ducky was prancing
about the lawn when Mickey came round the corner.
Ducky's mistress screamed. Mother and the children sat
in frozen horror, quite unable to do anything at all.
Ducky stood still and Mickey bore down upon him.

A thought flashed through Robin's mind. "Mickey's mouth! The puff-ball will make exactly one mouthful." But Mickey's mouth did not open. The puff-ball stood his ground. Mickey's great tail began to wag. The dogs met. They sniffed. The puff-ball's tail began to wag. Away over the lawn went the two dogs, the puff-ball yelping joyously.

"I'll never laugh at Ducky again," whispered Robin to Tim. "He ought to have a medal or something for standing still and letting a great giant like that come up to him."

The first week went by without any mishaps except that Mickey lay down in the middle of one of Mother's pet flower beds. When he got up there was a very large flat place.

"He has only to lie down a few more times," said Mother, "and there will be no garden at all." She looked at the flattened zinnias. "A steam roller couldn't have done better."

It was a little unfortunate, perhaps, that the butcher's bill came in on the day that Mickey had lain down in the garden.

"Listen to this," said Mother. "Four pounds of chopped meat — for Mickey. Six lamb chops — for us. Four pounds of chopped meat — for Mickey. One pot roast — for us. You see, Mickey eats more than we do! Something must be done about it." It was clear that Mother meant what she said.

That night Robin and Tim went to bed feeling very sad indeed. After they were in bed they could hear Father and Mother talking things over in the living room. Bits of the conversation floated in to them: " — can't possibly do it" — "another home" — "perhaps on a farm" — "the children will be upset." Robin cried herself to sleep.

The Portrait

The next day the weather was cooler than it had been for some time and the children set to work again on the wallpaper of Tim's room. Mickey lay watching them, his head on his paws. Already, he found his new home very satisfactory.

"Robin," said Tim as he peeled a long strip of wall-paper, "Mother didn't say anything about Mickey this morning, did she? Do you think she has changed her mind about him?"

"I'm afraid not," sighed Robin. "Oh, Tim, look at this funny bulge I've come to over the fireplace. What do you suppose it is?"

Tim came over to look.

Robin went on peeling and scraping. "Tim! It's canvas! Like Father's. It looks like the back of a picture."

"Sure does!" said Tim. "They must have used an old piece of canvas, or else a painting, to close up the stove hole and then papered over it. Easy, Robin!"

Carefully they pulled the canvas away from the wall. It was sooty and dusty, but it was a picture.

"Mother!" they shouted. "Come quickly! See what we have found."

Mother came hurrying in. She looked at the picture carefully, took a rag, and removed some of the dirt.

"It's an old portrait of a child," she said. "It might be valuable, and we'd better wait for Father. He will know just how to clean it."

Valuable! Robin and Tim looked at each other, the same thought racing through their minds. Perhaps it would mean at least a dozen square meals for Mickey!

Father was even more excited about the picture than the rest of the family. He cleaned it carefully. It was a portrait of a little fair-haired girl in a stiff brocaded dress.

"It must be quite old," said Robin.

"The face looks as if it didn't belong to the rest of the picture," said Tim.

"It didn't," said Father. "Traveling portrait painters used to paint the bodies and clothes on their canvases in the wintertime. Then, in the summer, the pictures were all ready to have the faces painted in. Of course the clothes didn't really suit the people who had their portraits painted. This little girl probably never wore such a handsome dress."

"How queer!" said Tim. "But, Father, do you think it's valuable?"

"I'm pretty sure it is," said Father. He looked at the large blank space over the big living-room fireplace. "It would go well there."

Tim and Robin looked at each other in despair.

"We thought — " began Robin.

"We hoped — " went on Tim.

"That we could sell the picture," said Robin. "The money would feed Mickey for at least a week."

"We must think this over," said Father. "You found it but of course I paid for the house, and so the picture is partly mine, isn't it?"

"I suppose so," said Tim slowly. "Then we ought to share the proceeds."

"That's the right way of it," said Father. "I tell you what we'll do. I'll agree that if the picture is really valuable, one half of the money shall go to feed Mickey for as long as it will last and one half shall be used on house improvements. You really share in those."

The children agreed that this plan was fair. Father rolled the picture up carefully and took it into town with him. The day seemed long, and the children got Mother and the car to Father's train fifteen minutes ahead of time. They walked slowly up and down the platform, with Mickey pacing behind them. Mickey was feeling snug and comfortable inside, for he had just finished four pounds of dinner. He knew, however, that something must be wrong because his young master and mistress seemed so worried. He tried licking their hands to see if that would help and it did seem to help a little. Robin put her arm around Mickey's neck and hugged him.

"You're such a lamb, Mickey. Suppose the picture isn't worth much and we can't keep you!"

The train was coming down the track. It stopped and Father got off. Two children and a dog rushed up to him so fast that Father almost lost his balance.

"Steady! Steady there! Remember you are three to one!"

"Father, oh, Father — is it?"

"Can we?"

"Was it — "

"It was," said Father, as they got into the car. "Quite valuable, though not so valuable as I expected. Anyway, your share will be enough to keep Mickey for a year — maybe longer. I also went to see a man who raises dogs and he told me about a good kennel food that's cheaper than meat. He says dogs do well on it and it will save us a lot of money. There's just one thing," he added, looking seriously at the children. "I am starting a bank account for you, and you may draw out enough for Mickey's food each month. But — what about the time when Robin wants a new book, or Tim wants something for his bicycle? What about ice-cream cones?"

By this time the car had turned in the gate and stopped in front of the door. Mickey was bounding joyfully across the lawn as if he knew that this was his home forever. Robin looked down across the valley. The red roof of the hot-dog stand seemed very inviting. But Robin shook her head.

"No," she said. "Not one penny goes for anything but dog food. And when it's all used up we'll find a way to get some more. Mickey is going to stay!"

Alice Dalgliesh

THE JUNIOR TEAM

THE Junior Baseball Team of Dover Village solemnly
filed out of town and into the country, thumping their bats
on the ground as they walked along.

Brick Evans said gloomily, "It was bad enough about
the uniforms, but it's the last straw about the house!"

The plan to have their fathers supply them with uniforms had failed. In almost every family an older brother had helped to veto the idea by saying that if anybody was going to buy uniforms it should be for an older team who could really play the game.

Neither fathers nor older brothers seemed to think it mattered that Elkton, the next town, was getting up a junior team, too, and that there was going to be a game between Elkton and Dover Village sometime during the summer.

Right on top of the disappointment about uniforms had come the information that the Van Hoosten country place, where the junior team had been practicing for two months, had been reduced another thousand dollars in price. That meant it might be sold at any time now, although it had been vacant for three years.

The house belonged to Ed Van Hoosten's grandfather and Ed was on the team.

"If the house is sold," said Brick to Ed, "then we won't even have a place to practice. My Dad says somebody will be sure to buy it, now that the price is lower, even if the land isn't any good. Flocks of people are looking for country property close to New York."

Ed's grandfather had suddenly become anxious to sell the house and go to California. Now there was talk of Ed's family moving, too.

"Why, we can't spare you!" said Brick. "We need you for the team."

They came to the first stone walls of the Van Hoosten

property. By that time Brick was filled with gloom from his toes to his head. There wasn't any prospect of uniforms. They might lose their one decent practice place, and they might even lose Ed, one of their best players.

Finally they came to the house itself, an old white Dutch colonial with green shutters that needed painting. In front of the house had been a white picket fence, but the fence was down, now, and broken in several places. Weeds were everywhere in the small front yard.

Ed found the key under a rock near the well at the side of the house. He went into the house, returning with a pail and a cup. As the boys pumped out drinks, a striped snake slid out of a hole in the corner of the house.

"I just hope that snake will show itself if anybody comes to look at this place today!" Brick said. The same snake had spoiled a sale a month ago.

The boys had been there last month when Mrs. Thomas, a real estate agent, had been showing the house. The woman looking at the house had seemed interested until the snake had appeared. Then she refused to consider the place another moment, saying she couldn't buy a house infested with snakes.

"And I hope the mosquitoes are out, too!" said Hal.

One person had rejected the place because she had been nearly eaten up by mosquitoes in the back yard. Mrs. Thomas had insisted that if the grass were cut, the mosquitoes would disappear, but that had not made a particle of difference. The woman said the back yard must be a perfect swamp.

The boys started out through waist-high grass to the baseball diamond. And a real diamond it was. They had cut the grass with a scythe, and then had done a lot of mowing. Now the place was nearly perfect, with the bases well marked, and plenty of space so that balls could stray as far as they pleased and not hurt anything except, perhaps, the barn, where the windows were all out, anyhow.

"Now remember!" Brick said, taking his place at bat. "We're going to play Elkton whether we have uniforms or not, see? We're going to get recognized in this town. The best way is to play a good game, with everybody working together, and not just for himself!"

They began to work in earnest. A short while later Brick noticed a light blue roadster, with the top down, drawn up to the side of the road. The driver stood by the stone wall looking at them.

"Not bad!" the man called out, and crawled over the wall.

"Hear that? Not bad!" said Hal, and tried to do some more of his fancy pitching.

"Look!" said the man, when Jim, at the bat, had hit Hal's ball and made a home run. "If you keep yourself loose, you'll do a better job. You're trying too hard and getting all tightened up." Then, before anyone had time to say anything, he continued, "This is the Van Hoosten place, isn't it?"

"That's right."

The man said he had stopped in town, and that the owner had told him the boys would show him the house.

"Oh!" said Brick, quickly. "You — you are interested in the house?" He glanced sidewise at the others. Then

he said, "Sure. We could show it to you, but it's probably nothing you'd want."

Since he had been around a good deal when the house had been shown, Brick knew most of the objections people had made to its condition. He began with the most common complaint, "There's no plumbing or water or electricity in the house. It's old."

"Well, let's have a look," said the man.

They all went back to the house.

"And the barn's not much good," added Jim.

"And the upstairs isn't finished off," said Hal, "and it's hot as blazes up there! They say it'd take a fortune to fix up just the upstairs alone."

Ed and the man went into the house first. Brick lingered outdoors a moment, muttering to Jim, "See to it that the cellar floor looks damp!" Nothing decided people against a place so much as a wet cellar.

Then Brick caught up with the others, suggesting that they go upstairs first.

It was almost unbearable up there, even though it was only morning. But the man did not seem to mind. He was looking at the wide, oak, hand-hewn beams with wooden pegs.

Finally they went downstairs, and the man knocked the walls with his knuckles.

"The outside walls are thin as paper," said Brick, remembering a comment he had heard. "You'd just have to make the walls all over."

"I guess there are woodchucks or something in the

house," said Ray, pointing to a hole in one corner of the room where they stood.

"None of the windows work very well," Hal put in. "I guess there'd have to be new windows everywhere."

Brick tried to hurry the man past the corner cupboard in the dining room. Everyone, even those who tried to find fault with the house, liked the corner cupboard, because it was something rare. But the man saw it and stood in front of it and deliberately scraped off some of the thick gray paint to have a look at the real wood. He looked a long time at the open beams, too, and at the fireplaces and the Dutch oven.

"They say it'd take a century to get all that paint off," Brick remarked.

The floors, wide oak boards, were uneven and rough.

"You could break your neck on these floors," said Ray.

Jim joined the group without the man's even seeming to notice it. Then they all went down into the cellar, the only cool place in the house. The man examined the sills and supports and remarked that the foundation was well built.

"But it's sort of damp down here," Brick replied. "I guess it's awfully hard to find just where a cellar does let in water."

"Well, thanks!" said the man, when they were out of the house again.

The snake did not appear, but Hal pointed to its hole. When there were snakes in a house, he said, he guessed it was pretty hard to get them out.

The man looked up at the roof, which sagged a bit in the middle.

The boys all knew that the sag was only because of the uneven beams beneath, but Jim said, "I'd sure hate to have that roof cave in on me!"

The man looked out back of the house.

"There are forty acres," said Ray, "but they're mostly stone. They say the land's not worth a thing."

"How long's the place been on the market?" the man asked.

"Oh, years!" said Brick, quickly. "And nobody's bought it, as you can see. They say it'd take a fortune to fix it up."

"That's why the owner reduced it a thousand dollars," said Jim. "And I guess he doesn't think it'll sell, even at that price."

"I don't know as he could even give it away," said Ray.

The man thanked them, saying it was a relief to have the real truth about a place. Then he mentioned the baseball field, saying, "You've got a pretty good diamond out there."

"We're signed up for a game with the Elkton Juniors," said Brick, with no little pride.

The man seemed interested. He even volunteered the information that he had a son about their age who was, if he did say so, pretty good when it came to baseball. He wished them luck and then went away.

"Well, I guess he's one person who won't buy the house," said Ed.

174

Then they forgot all about him until they went back to town again and stopped in at Ed's for a minute. Ed's grandfather asked if they had seen the man he had sent to look at the house.

"Yes, we showed him all the way through," said Ed, and began to talk about baseball.

But old Mr. Van Hoosten went on, "I said to myself, 'Those boys'll get a kick out of showing that man the house.'"

"Why?"

"Well, sir," said Mr. Van Hoosten, "that was Red Scranton!"

Red Scranton!

Brick gasped. So did everyone else. For Red Scranton was one of the most famous pitchers in the East. They had actually been in the presence of, they had been talking to, Red Scranton!

"Gee!" said Brick, and felt all the strength going out of his arms and legs. "He would have understood!" Red Scranton, with a boy of his own who played baseball, might even have let them continue to use the place for practice if he had bought it.

"How'd he like the house?" asked old Mr. Van Hoosten.

"He — didn't say," gulped Ed.

"We've got to get hold of him!" Brick kept thinking. Aloud, he said, "I — I suppose you have his address?"

Mr. Van Hoosten said he was sorry but he did not have the address.

Soon the boys were outdoors, and Brick was saying, "Think of having a person like Red Scranton living just half a mile away!"

"If his son was on our team, I'll bet he'd give us a few pointers!"

"We'd be the envy of every team, young or old, in the country," said Jim.

"We've got to get hold of his address," said Brick, "and write him a letter. No matter how hard it is, we've got to tell him the truth."

Ed suggested that he might have gone to one of the real estate agents in town to look for other property. So they divided up, some going to one agent, some to another. But no one had seen a Mr. Scranton.

Gloom settled over them. Nobody had an idea all afternoon or evening, and Brick even lay awake half the night. It was not until the next day that Jim thought of asking a New York newspaper to forward a letter to Red.

It took the junior team a whole day to frame a letter. Finally, however, the letter read:

DEAR MR. SCRANTON,

We didn't know who you were the day we showed you the house or it would have been different. The house is not as bad as we said it was. The truth is that we didn't want anybody to buy it because we might lose the baseball field. The field where the Dover Village men play

always has somebody on it, and so we don't have any other place to play except one where we broke a window two months ago and now we have to pay for the window.

There isn't any electricity in the house, it is true, but there is electricity in the road and it would be easy to have it in the house.

The roof won't cave in. It sags because of the hand-chopped beams underneath. People didn't use to measure things the way they do now. The house is an old Dutch colonial house and the truth is if anybody had money to fix it up it could be worth a lot of money.

The cellar was wet because one of us poured the water there purposely so you wouldn't buy the house.

It is a solid oak frame and people think it will last for-ever.

The well water is very good.

They say the mosquitoes will leave at once if the grass

is short. We will be glad to prove it by cutting the grass ourselves if you are interested. Only we must know if you are interested, because we don't want to cut the grass and then have somebody else come along and buy the house just because the yard is improved.

If you want to see the house again, let us know so we can cut the grass. If you don't want that house, please come and look at some others in Dover Village. Because we would like to have you live here and have your son on our team.

Very truly yours,
THE BOYS WHO SHOWED YOU THE
VAN HOOSTEN HOUSE

"You ought to sign it," Brick said, to Ed.

But Ed didn't want to. He said it would look as if he were boasting about his own family's house. So Brick put his own name and address below. Then he took an envelope, on which he wrote only "Mr. Red Scranton," sealed it, and enclosed it in another letter which he wrote to the Sports Editor of a New York paper.

Then followed days of waiting.

"What if he never gets it?"

"What if they sell the house to somebody else?"

"Maybe he can't get over the way we talked about the house! It was a pretty mean trick."

Presently there came a brief and businesslike note saying that Red Scranton might be driving up that way Sunday. If he did, he would be at the house around four o'clock.

"That means," said Brick, "that we'll have to cut the grass Saturday, and that means everybody that comes on Sunday is going to have the benefit. Suppose the house sells before Red gets here!"

But cut the grass on Saturday they did, borrowing all the scythes they could find, and three lawn mowers. They dragged away piles of dead wood. They came upon rose bushes and raspberry bushes and plants they knew must be flowers but could not identify. They propped up the picket fence. When they were right in the middle of doing that, Mrs. Thomas came with two persons and showed the house.

On Sunday Brick and the boys stationed themselves there as soon as they could get away after dinner. Sure enough, others came to look at the place. It was agony hearing Mrs. Thomas tell them how simple it was to do over a house.

About four o'clock the light blue roadster drew up. Red Scranton's wife and his son, Dick, were with him. Red suggested that the boys take Dick out to see the baseball diamond while he and his wife roamed through the house. He did not say a word about the letter.

So the boys took Dick to the diamond, telling him all about the junior team which, though it was having a struggle, was going to amount to something. They told about their need of uniforms and the discovery that their fathers weren't interested in uniforms for a team that had no reputation.

"But we're going to have a reputation, see?" added Ray.

"And we'd like to have you on the team," said Jim.

When they reached the house again, Mrs. Scranton was saying something about back terrace and corner cupboard and beams. But she stopped abruptly. Brick couldn't tell whether she liked the house or not.

Then the Scrantons went on their way.

"I don't think Red even told Dick about our letter," Jim said.

A week went by and there was no word from Red.

"Maybe he's bought some other house."

Another week passed.

Then, one afternoon, old Mr. Van Hoosten called the team over to his house.

"I've had an offer for my place," he said.

"Red Scranton?" asked everybody at once.

Mr. Van Hoosten nodded, and went on to explain that Mr. Scranton, as the boys knew, had not been shown the house by an agent. Therefore he, Mr. Van Hoosten, would not have to pay an agent's commission.

"Understand?" he asked.

The boys nodded, knowing that an agent expected to be paid a commission if he sold a house for anybody.

"But," continued Mr. Van Hoosten, "Mr. Scranton won't buy the house unless — "

Brick's heart sank.

"Unless I pay a commission to somebody," continued Mr. Van Hoosten. "Now you boys showed Mr. Scranton the house, but none of you has a broker's license. But," and there was a kind of twinkle in his eyes, "he suggests that I buy you a set of uniforms as your commission. And he proposes a campaign to get the town interested in junior baseball. One headed by Red Scranton!"

"What?" asked Brick. "You mean he'd go around drumming up interest himself? Go around to our fathers, for instance?"

"That's straight?" asked Jim.

"That's straight," said Mr. Van Hoosten. "It's all down in a letter, and I've never seen such a plain letter in all my life. It seems he won't even move into the neighborhood unless he thinks the town will show a little action regarding junior baseball."

"Gee!" said Brick. It was almost too much to believe.

Mr. Van Hoosten continued, "In addition, he wants the privilege of opening the first official junior team game."

"He has it!"

"He sure has!"

"Gee!" said Brick, again. If it was known that Red Scranton was at the game, not only Dover Village but all the other towns for miles around would come. Then he turned to his team and said quickly, "Listen, folks! It's going to be real training from now on, see? We've got to give the audience a good game."

Mr. Van Hoosten said, "Let's keep it to ourselves until it happens."

It was going to be hard, Jim said, but it was worth it.

"It's going to hit the town like an earthquake!" said Brick. There wasn't any other way of looking at it.

Chesley Kahmann

MARTIN lived with his grandfather and grandmother in a house in the middle of a great apple orchard. As far back as he could remember he had seen apple trees about him, covered with blossoms in spring, or bright with fruit, or gray-black against the snow. Orioles were nearly as common as robins on that farm, and in the autumn the deer came at dawn to eat the apples that had fallen to the ground. Martin had his especial friends among the trees, too — those that seemed to have planned their branches just for a boy to climb into green rooms above, where he might sit comfortably for hours.

The boy had no friends except the trees. There were no other children on the farm, and both his grandmother and grandfather were very busy. But one day Martin, playing by himself in the attic, came upon some old books that had been his father's when he was a little boy. After that Martin spent all the time he could in reading. His grandfather did not like that.

"Put that book down!" he said angrily one day when Martin was slow in coming to lunch. "You don't want to go around with your head full of silly stories, Martin. You'll never be a good apple man unless you are willing to work hard and keep your thoughts on apple trees. Hurry up now. This afternoon you can help me prune the east orchard."

Now Martin loved his grandfather more than anybody else. When he grew up he wanted to be just like him, master of the great orchard, but still the thoughts of the unfinished story kept going through his mind all that afternoon of early spring.

"Martin!" his grandfather had to say again and again. "Are you deaf, boy? I asked you to hand me up the pruning knife!"

But Martin could not keep his mind off the story. It was about a princess and a witch and spells and all sorts of exciting things. In trying to figure out the end of the story, Martin forgot to hold the foot of the ladder. He forgot to pile the pruned twigs where they could be burned. He put things in the wrong places and did not hear what was said to him and really was very irritating.

At last he did a terrible thing without meaning to do such a thing at all.

His grandfather was standing on a branch quite high up in a tree with the top rung of the ladder just below his feet. He called out something. Martin, who had been dreaming, did not hear exactly what it was, but jumped up and quickly took the ladder away and put it against the next tree. Now that was an extremely silly thing to do, and he would never have done it if he had been thinking. But his thoughts were still on the story of the witch.

A moment later he heard an exclamation, a snapping sound, and the crash of a fall behind him.

He turned with horror.

"Oh, Grandfather!" he cried, running to the figure on the ground.

"Where was that pesky ladder?" his grandfather demanded. "I thought you were steadying it as I told you to. You put it over there against another tree! Well, this is too much!"

The old man got to his feet and stood staring at Martin.

"I guess you're a fool," he said slowly, and turning without another word, limped back toward the farmhouse.

"I didn't mean to, Grandfather!" Martin called after him miserably.

"Fools never do," replied his grandfather, without stopping, and in a few moments he was lost to sight among the gray trunks and twisting branches of the apple trees.

It was cold outdoors, but Martin was too ashamed to want to go home. He wandered through the orchard of

McIntosh apples into the Baldwins and from there to the greenings on the other side of the hill. His grandfather had many kinds of apples to sell for different purposes: early apples for summer eating, late apples for winter eating, some for cooking, and others for drying or making jelly.

"The perfect apple hasn't been found yet," the old man used to say. "And probably won't be in our time," he would add. "I try out the new kinds I hear about, but there's always something wrong about each one."

Martin, cold and miserable, stood for a moment on the hilltop looking over the rolling orchards beneath him.

"I wish I could find the perfect apple," he thought. "Then Grandfather wouldn't think I was a fool. He would prize the perfect apple more than a crown."

For a moment, thinking about "crown" made him think about the unfinished story, but he pushed the thought from his mind. It had made trouble enough.

He had never been so far away from the farmhouse before, except to go to the village. He looked about him now. Not far beyond him stood a small red farmhouse in a field in which young junipers were beginning to grow. Smoke came from the chimney but he could see no one around.

"That must be where Miss Tildy Thomas lives. I've heard Grandmother speak of her," he thought, and was just going to turn sadly toward home when he heard a cat mew on the stone wall near at hand.

Martin liked cats and looked in the direction of the sound. He was gazing straight into the eyes of a little old woman whose head was almost on the level of the stone wall. She was bent nearly double and leaned on a stick, and looked exactly like the pictures of the witch in his book except that she was wearing an old red sweater.

"What's the matter?" she said sharply. "I won't bite you. I suppose you're Martin. Well, Martin, I'm Tildy Thomas and this is Thomas Thomas, my cat. I came out to see if I could pull up some of these junipers that are spoiling my hayfield but I've got more rheumatism than strength these days. I'm better off inside."

Martin said nothing. Tildy Thomas gave him another sharp look from her face that was on a level with his own.

"You're cold, too," she said suddenly. "Come in and I'll give you some cambric tea and cookies."

Martin could not refuse a polite invitation like that, but his heart beat fast as he followed the old woman and her cat back to the little red house. Inside, everything was wonderfully neat. Colored hens' eggs in crocheted bags hung in a cluster from the middle of the mantel. There were starched white cloths on the arms and backs of each of the chairs. Over the pictures on the walls hung lace curtains, drawn back and tied with bright ribbons. As a result, one seemed to be looking out of windows, sometimes straight out to the sea, where a vessel was being wrecked in a thunderstorm, or stranger still, at the large photographs of the Thomas relatives, who had the air of peering back at one through panes of glass.

Martin did not know much about witches' houses. Certainly he felt very strange in this room.

"If I try to run away," he thought, "all those faces between the lace curtains will call out to tell her I'm going." So he decided to stay where he was.

In a little time the old woman hobbled back with a tray which she put on a low table. She had to sit down very slowly because of her rheumatism.

"Something hot will taste good," was all she said, as she poured him out a cup of cambric tea, made of hot water and milk with a big teaspoonful of honey in it. Now that she was sitting down she looked more like other people. She drank her own tea. There was a big pile of cookies on a plate.

"I hope there are no spells in them," Martin thought to himself as he ate. But, looking up, he was surprised to see what a nice face old Tildy Thomas really had. Soon she began to ask him why he was unhappy and he told her.

"Hmm," she said, nodding.

"I don't want Grandfather to think I'm a fool!" Martin cried out.

For a little while Tildy said nothing.

"Don't you worry," she said at last. "Things change. They aren't today what they were yesterday or what they will be tomorrow. As I see it, you should keep your mind on thinking that you want to be a good orchard man like your grandfather, and some day things will be all right."

"Are you sure?" Martin asked anxiously.

"Certain," said old Tildy, with such assurance that he felt comforted.

"I've got troubles, too," she went on. "I get lonely."

"Do you?" Martin asked eagerly. "So do I. Would you like me to bring over some of my books? They help loneliness a lot. We could talk them over together."

"I'd like it very much," said the old woman.

After that, Martin and Tildy Thomas became great friends. The boy often went over to see her and helped her to do the things she could not do herself, like sweeping down the cobwebs from the corners of the ceiling and beating the rugs. He even tugged up most of the junipers around the house.

"I do hate to see them in the hay," she said. "Even though no one cuts the hay any more. Still, it's no place for junipers."

Then she would give him tea and cookies or chocolate cake, and meantime they would talk about the books he had brought her.

It was different helping Tildy from working at home. Tildy needed help. At home Grandfather and Grandmother could get along faster if Martin weren't in their way at all, but as the weeks went on, the boy learned all sorts of things in helping Tildy. Even his grandfather said once or twice, "You're getting handy about the place, Martin," but still the old man could not quite forget the way in which the boy had taken the ladder almost from under his feet.

A Friendly Witch

Summer came and passed. Martin would have been happy if only he could have felt that he had his grandfather's respect.

"You're still worrying over what your grandfather thinks about you," Tildy said to him one day. "I have a feeling something's going to happen that will please him. I don't exactly know what it is, Martin, but you keep your wits about you and it's bound to happen. Now I think I'll go in and rest. Did you ever go up Scratchy Hill back of my house? Why don't you and Thomas go exploring?"

It was a beautiful September day, soft and golden. Thomas and Martin climbed the hill slowly, up a little path that led back of the old chicken houses. The land was grown up to pines and a few hemlocks, with beeches now and then, their leaves yellow against the tight gray of their bark. After a while, the boy and cat came upon a sort of clearing. There was a hollow place where a cellar had once been, and some tiger lilies gone wild from a forgotten garden. One could still see the heap of bricks that had once been the chimney. Over beyond, by the tumbledown wall, there were some young apple seedlings in a thicket around old stumps where the orchard had been.

While the cat hunted hopefully for rabbits by the spring, Martin stood looking about him. He was thinking of the people who must have lived here once long ago, wondering who they had been and what they had looked like. Maybe they were early Thomases with fine gray eyes like Miss Tildy's.

Suddenly he seemed to hear her voice in his ears, "You keep your wits about you." It was what she had said to him that afternoon. What would a boy do who had his wits about him, he wondered anxiously.

Was there maybe a treasure under the fallen chimney? Ought he to begin digging?

Or was there maybe a bear hidden behind that big oak and ought he to run?

190

Or had something fallen into the cellar that couldn't
get out? But there was nothing in the cellar.

The only thing that visited the clearing seemed to be
deer. He saw their tracks in the soft ground by the spring.
Perhaps they came for water, but more likely for the wild
apples.

Apples! Maybe that was what she meant.

But everyone knew wild apples were bitter dwarf things.
Why should he taste a wild apple? Still, he'd better do it,
he thought. There didn't seem to be anything else for a
boy with his wits about him to do.

Martin picked up one of the apples and bit into it. He had been used to apples all his life but he had never tasted one like this. It was a bright red apple, just running over with sap that tasted as though it had spice in it. He took another bite and it was just as good. Sometimes nature takes a hand and mixes her seed better than men can. The McIntosh apple itself came from a wild strain, Martin remembered, as he excitedly filled his hat with the best he could find.

He went running down the path with Thomas Thomas tearing helter-skelter after him.

"Miss Tildy! Miss Tildy!" he shouted, long before she could possibly hear him. "I've found it! I've found it! The perfect apple!"

He saw her figure bent over in the doorway, her poor face near the handle of the door.

"Good luck!" she called to him. "Don't stop! Tell me about it later."

He climbed the wall, and ran over the hill, stumbling and panting, down through the orchard. His grandfather was yoking the white oxen in the farmyard. He looked up frowning as they jerked their heads at Martin's noisy approach.

"No need to startle the creatures," the old man scolded.

"Grandfather! Grandfather!" Martin shouted. "Taste this! Taste it!"

Martin's grandfather would always taste a new apple. He took one from Martin's hat and bit into it. A surprised look came over his face. Then he took another bite.

"Where'd you get that apple, Martin?" he asked as though he were in church.

Martin could tell he had not been mistaken. This apple was a wonder.

"Back of Miss Tildy's, on Scratchy Hill," he said. "Like it, Grandfather?"

Martin's grandfather took another thoughtful bite.

"I should say," he admitted slowly, "that apple seems to be just — about — perfect. I guess that one apple is worth more than our whole orchard. You've made apple history today, Martin."

Martin remembered something.

"It was Miss Tildy who told me to go up there and keep my wits about me," he said. "I wonder if she knew."

"It's hard to be sure what Miss Tildy knows," agreed the grandfather, taking another bite of the apple. "Come along, Martin, we've got to tell Grandmother the good news." He left the oxen without glancing at them, the half-eaten apple in one hand, and the other on Martin's shoulder.

But it was Miss Tildy Thomas who gave the new apple its name when they all went to see her later in the day.

"That's a pretty good Scarlet Martin," she said, biting into one. "Lucky the boy found it. But boys are always lucky who make friends with witches."

Then she laughed as though she had made a joke, but Martin was not so sure that it was a joke after all.

Elizabeth Coatsworth

CAROLINA POSSUM HUNT

SELL enough hides to amount to eight dollars and forty-nine cents!" Burrus Englehard looked down at his sister in amazement. "Why, my dear girl, possum hides sell for only twenty-five cents apiece. You'd have to wipe out all the possums in this neighborhood to get that many hides."

Ellen shook her head. "I don't care. I've got to have that money. Now, Burrus, please! Please won't you take me possum hunting?"

"What do you want the money for?"

"Well," Ellen began unwillingly, "I want a taffeta party dress. All the girls are getting them, but Mama says it's too expensive. So if I want one, I'll have to earn the money. I've racked my brains for ways and means, and possum

hunting is the only thing I can think of. Please, Burrus, won't you take me?"

She glanced up at her brother with a pleading look. Donis, the big black Newfoundland dog, lifted his head also and gazed at Burrus with melting brown eyes, as though adding his plea to that of his young mistress.

The three were sitting on the front steps of the Englehard home in the North Carolina lowlands, facing the slow-moving Pamlico River, which could be seen shining through an avenue of twisted live oaks. The house was surrounded on the other three sides by snowy cotton fields.

Burrus crossed his legs and gazed out over the water. "Well," he said finally, "I suppose I could take you — only girls get scared so easy. It's pretty lonesome out there in the swamp at night. You'd be shaking in your shoes if you so much as heard a hoot-owl screech. And maybe you would step on a snake. What would you do then?"

Ellen hid a shiver. "I won't step on any snakes, Burrus. And I promise I won't be scared."

"Well," said Burrus again, doubtfully, "Jim Padget and I were aiming to go possum hunting tonight, as a matter of fact. Jim's borrowed old Jed Towle's possum dogs. Maybe, if you're sure — "

His sister gave a little squeal of delight. "That couldn't be better! But why do we have to have Jed's possum dogs? Donis could tree a possum, I know he could."

"Him!" cried Burrus. "You might as well have an elephant lumbering through the bushes and scaring all the animals out of the woods." He bent down and rubbed the Newfoundland's ears. "You're a good boy, Donis, but you wouldn't qualify as a possum dog."

As soon as it was dark, the hunters set out for the woods. They were a party of four, for Ellen had persuaded her brother and his chum to allow Eulalie Wilson, her best friend, to join the expedition. Their consent came a little unwillingly, however, for Eulalie could always be depended upon to get scared of everything.

Jim and Burrus each carried a gun, and Ellen shouldered an ax which was to be used for cutting down the tree in case the possum took to such a refuge. In the yellow glow of a lantern which swung from Burrus's arm, two possum dogs strained ahead at the ends of rope leashes. As the quartet picked their way through the moonlit fields, long, mournful wails broke in occasionally upon their talk.

Donis, shut up in the barn, was giving voice to his disappointment.

On the edge of the woods the young people felt a shiver of uneasiness as they always did upon entering the swampy, jungle-like forest of the Carolina lowlands. It was gloomy enough in the daytime, with dark pines and cypresses towering upward, live oaks crouching like gnarled old men, and heavy vines coiled around the tall tree trunks. At night it seemed positively frightening.

The only carefree members of the party were the dogs. They were eagerly sniffing at the ground.

"Might as well let them go," said Burrus, untying their ropes. The hounds made off briskly. The young people followed, their swinging lantern making the long shadows of the tree-trunks weave and leap about in a strange witches' dance. Soon they came into a section of rustling palmetto bushes which made going so slow that the dogs soon left them behind.

"Listen!" ordered Burrus, stopping suddenly. "Maybe we can follow them by ear." But the hounds went silently. There was not a sound but the humming of insects.

"Looks as though we'd lost 'em," said Jim.

"Yes," agreed Burrus, "and there's no use plunging along blindly. We'd better find a good place to sit down and wait. They'll let us know soon enough when they've found something."

Struggling through the palmetto, they came out at last into a clear space underneath a large holly tree.

"No telling how long we'll have to wait," said Jim. He

noticed that Ellen was beginning to shiver in the chill autumn air. "Let's build a fire."

Everyone set to work gathering twigs and branches, and soon a fire was well started. The hunters began to take heart as they all gathered about it, holding out their chilled hands to the blaze and munching on some molasses cookies which Ellen had brought along.

The dark spell of the woods almost dissolved in the cheerful glow, but it crept again into the circle of firelight when Burrus remarked lightly, "I wonder if there are any wildcats or panther cats now in these woods."

"I don't know," Jim answered. "But old Jed Towle says a pack of wildcats attacked a hunter friend of his who was camping on the banks of the Pamlico River. Jed said the man crawled underneath his overturned canoe, but the cats kept clawing under to get at him. He spent the night hitting at their paws with his hatchet. I wouldn't know whether the story was true or not. You know old Jed."

Eulalie had huddled closer to Ellen as the tale proceeded, and even Burrus cast an uneasy glance over his shoulder into the darkness. Suddenly an unearthly yelp rent the air, followed by another and another. The two boys came to their feet with a leap.

"They've scented one!" Burrus shouted, jumping upon the fire and stamping it out.

"Scented one?" Ellen stared at him.

"Sure, silly! The dogs have scented a possum. They're on his trail. Come on!"

Before the two girls fully realized what had happened, they were on their way, dashing through the bushes, struggling along after the boys. The brambles tore at them. Once Eulalie slipped in a swampy place and fell, but nothing mattered now except the chase. The dogs were running, baying loudly. The boys were shouting and urging them on. The trail of the possum was confusing. It circled and doubled back, again and again.

"Say," Jim panted, laying a restraining hand on Burrus's arm, "I don't like this! It's not like a possum to dodge about like this. A possum's slow. When he finds out the dogs are after him, he takes to the first tree in sight."

But Burrus scarcely heard him. His ear was turned toward the baying dogs. "Listen!" he interrupted. "They're over to the right. Come on!" Dragging his reluctant friend by the arm, he plunged again toward the direction of the chase.

Just when Ellen's lungs were ready to burst and she felt she could not take another step, the tone and tempo of the barking suddenly changed. It became high-pitched and excited, spurring the boys to an even faster pace.

"They've treed him," Burrus shouted.

To her own surprise, Ellen found breath to follow.

"They've got one, girls, a big one!" Jim called out as he reached the spot.

Pushing through the myrtle bushes, Ellen and Eulalie

moved into the circle of light cast by Burrus's lantern at the foot of a bent old live oak. The dogs were running about the tree barking furiously. Now and then they leaped up on the rough trunk in a frenzied effort to get at the quarry hidden in its branches.

"Where's the possum?" asked Ellen, peering into the clump of dark leaves.

"There on that limb. Can't you see his eyes shine?" Jim pointed out two balls of light which stared steadily downwards.

"Oh, goodness! Yes, I see them. Are you sure it's a possum?" Ellen asked, edging nervously away from the excited group. Those eyes seemed to hold a more evil glare than might be expected from a timid possum.

"Of course it's a possum, silly!" Burrus exclaimed. "What else takes to a tree when it's cornered?" But Ellen was not satisfied, and kept stepping back still farther into the shadows.

"Come on, Jim, let's try to shake him out," cried Burrus. He and his friend laid hold of the tree trunk, but tug as they might, the tree did not so much as quiver, and the boys stopped, winded by their efforts.

"That's no good," shouted Jim above the din of the hounds, "and there's no use trying to cut it down. There's no harder wood on earth than live oak. We'd never get an ax into it."

"Then how are you going to get him?" Eulalie cried. She knew well enough that shooting a possum out of a tree was not the proper way to get one.

"Come on, Jim, give me a shove. I'm going up and shake the limb," Burrus answered her question indirectly. Kicking off his boots, he began to climb up the old bent trunk.

"Wait a minute," Jim urged. "We'd better make dead sure what's up there first."

At this, Ellen crept still farther into the darkness. But Burrus shook off his friend's hand. He climbed until he reached the limb on which the animal was crouching. From opposite sides of the tree, Jim and Eulalie watched breathlessly as he began to hump himself along it.

"Can you see what it is yet?" Jim asked.

"No, but it's a possum all right, and I'll have him down in a moment. Now, look out, I'm going to give the limb a shake!" They could hear Burrus bouncing himself up and down in an effort to shake off the animal.

Suddenly Eulalie let out a terrified screech. "That's not a possum! He just stuck his head out of the leaves. It's a great big yellow creature!"

"You're always seeing things, Eulalie," Burrus called down in scorn. He grunted, giving the branch a mighty heave.

As he did so, a great catlike animal launched itself from the limb. It came flying through the air in a tremendous leap. For a moment it gleamed tawny gold as it flashed through the circle of light. Then it disappeared like a shot into the darkness beyond.

In the commotion about the tree, Ellen had not been missed. As the beast jumped straight toward her hiding place, her shrill scream rang out from the shadows.

Jim leaped toward the sound. In the darkness he stumbled upon the fallen girl, her arms clasped tightly above her head.

"Ellen! Are you hurt?" he cried, bending over her, the lantern held high.

"She's dead! Dead!" screamed Eulalie. "That beast has killed her. He's torn her limb from limb!"

Cautiously, Ellen's arm moved, and one eye peered forth.

"Is it gone?" she whispered.

"Sure it's gone," Jim answered. "Are you all right?"

Ellen sat up, feeling of herself here and there. "That creature jumped right on me. He knocked me down and ran right over me."

At this moment, Burrus, whose view had been cut off by leaves, came bustling into the midst of the crowd.

"What's the matter? What happened to the possum? The dogs can't find him."

"Possum!" exclaimed Eulalie. "Just as I told you, that wasn't any possum. It was a panther cat. And he jumped right on Ellen."

"Panther cat! A puma!" gasped Ellen, frightened at the realization that so dreaded a beast had used her for a foot mat. If the puma had leaped for her on purpose he could easily have stripped her to pieces with a few strokes of his powerful hind claws. Fortunately for her, the beast had leaped blindly, confused by the lights, and with only one thought — to escape.

The hounds were now left perplexed, without a trail. They kept sniffing at the base of the tree, circling wider and wider about it in an attempt to pick up the place where the beast had landed. Without warning, a sudden hue and cry broke loose among them. The dogs had found the trail at last, and they set off in haste after their prey.

"Say, Jim, look! They're after him," Burrus shouted. "They've got him on the jump! Let's go!" Snatching up his gun and the lantern from the ground, he dashed head-long after the dogs.

"Boom! Boom!" In a moment the woods rang with thundering echoes of a gun.

"Hey!" Jim shouted after him. "Come back here! We can't take these girls after a panther cat. It's too dangerous."

Burrus reappeared, leaping over the bush, his eyes wide with excitement.

"Here!" he cried, handing the lantern to Ellen. "Take this, and the gun. And stay right here. You'll be all right. Come on, Jim! Bring your flashlight." Without waiting for an answer, he went bounding off into the darkness.

For a moment Jim hesitated, but the wild yelping of the dogs and Burrus's eager calls were too much for him. Throwing caution to the winds, he plunged after his friend.

PANTHER HUNT

The boys had gone off in such a hurry that there had been no time for argument or objections.

"Well, a fine pair they are!" Ellen exclaimed in disgust. Then she looked down at the gun which she held gingerly in her two hands. "Do you know how to shoot, 'Lalie?"

"Burrus let me shoot that gun once. But I wouldn't do it again. It knocked me right off my feet."

"Oh, well, there isn't any danger so long as we have the lantern," Ellen comforted herself. "Animals are afraid of fire."

"That's not fire, that's light."

"It's one and the same," Ellen replied.

After that a silence fell between them, while they listened to the distant sounds of the chase. Ellen slid down and sat leaning against a tree. No possum hides and no taffeta party dress would result from this trip, she decided, not with the boys off after a panther cat. It would be hours before they returned, if they ever did. She fell to wondering how she and Eulalie would get home if the boys did not come back. At the moment she had not the faintest idea which way was east and which was west. And what if some animal should come after them? She clasped her hands nervously in her lap.

"I hear something coming," Eulalie whispered.

"Hush up!" Ellen replied. "There's nothing." But there was a lack of assurance in her tone, for, in the distance, a crackling of the underbrush could be faintly heard.

"It might be the boys coming back," she whispered, after the sounds had grown too loud to deny.

"No, it's not. It's that panther. He's scented us and he's coming back to get us!"

"It's not, either. Panther cats don't make any noise."

"Then it's a bear. That's what it is, a bear!"

"Well, there's no use to be afraid," said Ellen, swallowing hard. "We've still got the lantern. Nothing will bother us so long as that keeps burning."

Even as she spoke, the lantern began to flicker dangerously. Ellen snatched it up and gave the wick a hasty turn. The light only sputtered and grew dimmer.

"The oil's out!" she cried aloud in dismay, forgetting to whisper.

One bright flare was the lantern's dying effort. Then blackness enclosed them. From the increased rustling of the bushes, the bear — or whatever it was — must be fairly upon them.

"The gun!" Ellen cried. "Get out of the way, Eulalie, I'm going to fire it." She placed the stock against a tree to save herself from the shock, and then pulled the trigger. No sound resulted. Desperately she snapped first one trigger and then the other. The gun refused to fire.

"It's empty!" she cried, throwing it on the ground. "Don't you remember? Burrus shot it twice when he went after the panther."

"The bear! Here he comes!" shrieked Eulalie.

The sound of Ellen's voice had seemed to lend speed to the creature's feet. In the moonlight filtering through the branches, the two terrified girls caught sight of a dark, shaggy form crashing toward them.

"Run, run!" cried Ellen, taking to her heels. "Help, Burrus! Help, Jim! A bear!"

She fled wildly, tearing through brambles, bumping into tree trunks, while the beast kept gaining on her. Her breath began to come in painful gasps, her heart to pound with such thumps that she knew she could not hold out much longer. There was no escape. When at last she tripped and fell, she did not have the heart to struggle up again.

She felt the hot breath of the animal upon her neck. A cold nose thrust itself into her ear, a shaggy mane brushed her neck, and a warm tongue licked across her face. Unconsciously, she put up an arm to ward it off as she often did when Donis tried to caress her. Then, in the midst of her terror, a familiar doggy smell reached her nose, like the smell of Donis after he had been out in the rain.

"Is that you, Donis?" she asked in a trembling voice.

"Woof! Woof!" came the reply in a joyous bark.

A wave of relief spread over Ellen, which, in turn, gave way to a feeling of anger.

"You rascal!" she cried, scrambling to her feet. "You've scared me out of seven years' growth."

It took loud and determined shouting to recall Eulalie, but she returned at last, still in a state of terror.

"Where's the bear? Where's the bear?" she kept asking over and over.

"I tell you there was no bear," Ellen told her for the fifth time. "It was Donis. He must have broken out of the barn and trailed me."

"But where's the bear? I saw a bear!"

Ellen seized Eulalie's plump arm and shook it. "Now you listen to me, Eulalie. Don't you tell the boys about this. If they found out that we mistook poor old Donis for a bear, we'd never hear the last of it. You're not to tell. Do you understand?"

Eulalie promised hastily.

They did not have long to wait for the boys. They came whooping through the woods, their flashlight cutting

the darkness. "Hey, Ellen! Eulalie! Where are you?"

"Here."

"Are you all right?" Jim called anxiously as the two came through the trees.

"We thought we heard you yelling about a bear," Burrus panted.

"A bear? Oh, no, I was just calling to you because the lantern went out."

"There was a bear. He came right at us," Eulalie interrupted. "He took right after us and — " Ellen's nails, digging suddenly into her arm, cut her off abruptly.

Burrus was bewildered. He turned the flashlight full upon his sister. Her appearance amazed him.

"What's happened here?" he cried, stepping back. "You're all scratched up. Your clothes are in strings. Why, you look as though you'd been run through the corn sheller. And what's Donis doing here?"

"That bear! He took right after us!" Eulalie began again.

At this Burrus broke into a shout of laughter. "Oh, I see. Catch on, Jim? When old Donis came up in the dark, they thought he was a bear. Ha! Ha! Ha! They tore themselves all to pieces running away from him."

Jim caught on. The two boys leaned against a tree, howling with laughter.

Presently Burrus's face sobered. "Say, Ellen, what did you do with my gun?"

"I don't know," Ellen replied angrily. "You left it empty. I threw it down."

"You threw it down!" Burrus's voice rose and broke on a high note. "Here, give me that flash, Jim. I'm going to find my gun."

As he whistled for the hounds and disappeared into the darkness, Ellen sank to the ground. She felt weary and disappointed.

"Seems as if everything short of sudden death has happened to me tonight," she sighed, "and I've got nothing to show for it but bruises and scratches. Not even one measly little hide."

"Why, Ellen, you've got your hide," Jim replied.

He got up and dragged a heavy body into a patch of moonlight.

"Why, Jim! You got the panther cat!" Ellen cried, viewing the limp form with amazement.

"Of course, and a panther skin will sell for plenty for us all."

"Will my share bring as much as eight dollars and forty-nine cents?"

"Sure. Maybe more."

"Hurrah!" Ellen shouted. No need for saving, adding penny to nickel and nickel to dime! The entire sum she needed was practically in her hands. "Hurrah!"

Presently Burrus returned and they all started on the long tramp back home. The two boys and Eulalie laughed and joked, while Ellen said scarcely a word. She was busily imagining the beautiful taffeta dress she would wear to the next school party.

Ellis Credle

SONGS OF GREATNESS

COLUMBUS

BEHIND him lay the gray Azores;
   Behind, — the Gates of Hercules;
Before him not the ghost of shores,
   Before him only shoreless seas.
The good mate said: "Now must we pray,
   For lo! the very stars are gone.
Brave Admiral, speak; what shall I say?"
   "Why, say: 'Sail on! sail on! and on!'"

"My men grow mutinous day by day;
   My men grow ghastly wan and weak."
The stout mate thought of home; a spray
   Of salt wave washed his swarthy cheek.
"What shall I say, brave Admiral, say,
   If we sight naught but seas at dawn?"
"Why, you shall say, at break of day:
   'Sail on! sail on! sail on! and on!'"

They sailed and sailed, as winds might blow,
  Until at last the blanched mate said:
"Why, now not even God would know
  Should I and all my men fall dead.
These very winds forget their way,
  For God from these dread seas is gone.
Now speak, brave Admiral, speak and say — "
  He said: "Sail on! sail on! and on!"

They sailed. They sailed. Then spake the mate:
  "This mad sea shows his teeth tonight;
He curls his lips, he lies in wait,
  With lifted teeth, as if to bite;
Brave Admiral, say but one good word.
  What shall we do when hope is gone? "
The words leaped like a leaping sword:
  "Sail on! sail on! sail on! and on!"

Then, pale and worn, he kept his deck,
  And peered through darkness. Ah, that night
Of all dark nights! And then a speck —
  A light! a light! a light! a light!
It grew, a starlit flag unfurled!
  It grew to be Time's burst of dawn.
He gained a world; he gave that world
  Its grandest lesson: "On! sail on!"

Joaquin Miller

THE BOY WASHINGTON

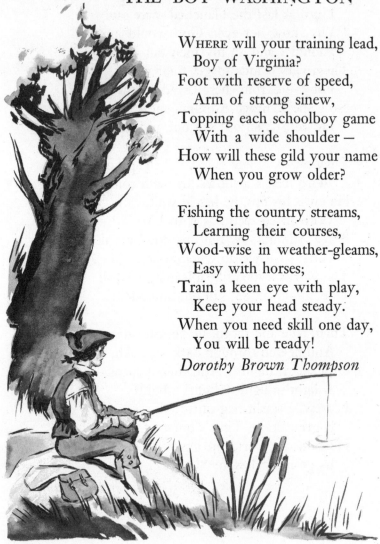

WHERE will your training lead,
  Boy of Virginia?
Foot with reserve of speed,
  Arm of strong sinew,
Topping each schoolboy game
  With a wide shoulder —
How will these gild your name
  When you grow older?

Fishing the country streams,
  Learning their courses,
Wood-wise in weather-gleams,
  Easy with horses;
Train a keen eye with play,
  Keep your head steady.
When you need skill one day,
  You will be ready!

Dorothy Brown Thompson

ABRAHAM LINCOLN

REMEMBER he was poor and country-bred;
  His face was lined; he walked with awkward gait.
Smart people laughed at him sometimes and said,
  "How can so very plain a man be great?"

Remember he was humble, used to toil,
  Strong arms he had to build a shack, a fence,
Long legs to tramp the woods, to plow the soil,
  A head chuck-full of backwoods common sense.

Remember all he ever had he earned.
  He walked, in time, through stately White House doors;
But all he knew of men and life he learned
  In little backwoods cabins, country stores.

Remember that his eyes could light with fun;
  That wisdom, courage set his name apart;
But when the rest is duly said and done,
  Remember that men loved him for his heart.

Mildred Meigs

CLARA BARTON

Brave Clara Barton
Stood beside her door,
And watched young soldiers
March away to war.

"The flags are very fine," she said,
"The drums and trumpets thrilling.
But what about the wounds
When the guns start killing?"

Clara Barton went to work
To help keep men alive,
And never got a moment's rest
Till eighteen-sixty-five.

She washed and she bandaged,
She shooed away the flies,
She hurried in nurses,
She begged for supplies.

She cared for the wounded
And comforted the dying,
With no time for sleep
And still less for crying.

Clara Barton went abroad
When the war was ended,
Hoping for a little peace
Now that things had mended.

Clara found, as soon
As her foot touched shore,
That she'd come just in time
For the Franco-Prussian War.

After that her life, for her,
Held but little rest,
With famine in the East
And earthquakes in the West.

Floods, drowning Johnstown,
Hurricanes in Texas,
Fires, out in Michigan,
Things that fright and vex us.

In between the hurry calls,
Never at a loss,
She founded and established
The merciful Red Cross.

Battle, murder, sudden death,
Called for Clara Barton.
No one ever called in vain.
Clara was a Spartan.

Rosemary Benét

CABINS IN THE CLEARING

THE PURITAN CAT

T HE Deacon's Cat was very fond of her master. She realized in her cattish way that he was an important man. She thought that the government of the Province depended largely upon him, and caused him to work hard all the week.

He had his peculiar habits, of course, but the Cat had learned to expect these among men. For instance, on Sunday he never did any work, and on that day he would not even pet the Cat. After returning from church, he would sit quietly and read in a great black-covered book practically all the rest of the day. The Cat thought it must be a very wise book, for the Deacon always consulted it when people came to him for advice.

Every Saturday night, the Deacon had a cold roast put

aside to serve as his Sunday dinner, and an extra saucer of milk placed on the floor, which was for the Cat's Sunday dinner.

The Cat, seeing no sense in saving it, lapped up the milk in both saucers right away and polished the dishes with her tongue. So naturally by morning she was hungry again.

However, she had ways of getting food, and she never worried about filling her stomach until the Deacon's Sister came to live with them. For the Deacon's Wife had gone to Heaven, and his Sister had arrived in Massachusetts to sew on the buttons that would come off his clothes, and to sweep up the dust that would settle on the furniture.

The Deacon had never paid any attention to the Sunday behavior of the Cat until his Sister came. Then, one morning, as he was waiting for that lady to get her bonnet strings tied properly so as to accompany him to church, he caught a glimpse of the Cat under his English rosebush, eating something which proved to be a bird.

"You did not catch that bird on the Sabbath Day, did you?" asked the Deacon, as he glanced over his shoulder to see whether his Sister had noticed. Then, picking up what was left of the feathered heap, he tossed it far out in the river, at the same time scolding the Cat softly so that his Sister might not hear.

"Never, never catch anything to eat on the Sabbath Day, for that would be work. And to work on the Sabbath is a sin." He added, "My Sister is particular."

The Cat knew already that the Sister was very particular. In fact, ever since she had arrived with her needle and her broom, the Cat had found it more comfortable to spend most of the time out of the house while the Deacon was at work. In spite of these absences, she had heard the Sister declare that the house would be much cleaner if the Cat were given away, because she brought in a great deal of dust and even mud.

The Deacon would not listen to such a proposal. "Why, the Cat is very clean," he had said, "and besides, she is as good and as intelligent as any person."

"Hmm," said the Sister. "I suppose the Cat even keeps the Sabbath."

"I have never noticed her doing otherwise," replied the Deacon.

"I have my own ideas," said the Sister, picking a cat hair off the Deacon and holding it up to the light so that he would be sure to see it.

"Ideas are not evidence," said the Deacon, and that was that.

So it was no wonder the good man was rather upset at finding the half-eaten bird and the Cat under the English rosebush. Though of course, he reminded himself, the bird might have lain there since the day before. So long as it was not caught on the Sabbath, it was not a sin to eat it on that day.

After he had explained very carefully to the Cat that she must never work on the seventh day, he thought no more about the matter.

The Sister never knew about the bird, but she was determined to get rid of the Cat. One day she brought up the subject again.

"I notice the Cat always drinks all her milk on Saturday night. Now where do you suppose she gets food on Sunday, unless — "

"She is probably not hungry after a double meal on Saturday," snapped the Deacon. "Or," he added after a bit, "perhaps she fasts."

The Sister sniffed a most expressive sniff.

After that the Cat noticed one or two rather peculiar things. Every Saturday the Deacon's Sister, as soon as she had cleaned the whole living room very carefully, would slip small pieces of cheese under the edge of the braided rug, and behind the rush broom by the fireplace. The Deacon was a little near-sighted and he never noticed, not even when he happened to move the rush broom.

It was rather kind of the Sister to leave the cheese, thought the Cat at first, for it certainly attracted the mice. On Sundays when the Deacon and his Sister had gone to church, and the house and the Cat were perfectly still, one or two mice were sure to come slipping in, their noses twitching at that delightful fragrance of cheese in the air. If a mouse came alone, it never left the room, and if two came, only one mouse was ever seen to depart.

Now the Cat must have remembered about the scolding, for when she caught a mouse, she ate every bit of it in a great hurry, and somehow she always was half asleep on her cushion when the Deacon's Sister returned.

That was another queer thing. Every Sunday the Sister would manage to get home before the Deacon. She would arrive, quite breathless, and tiptoe up the walk outside and past the English rosebush. She would rest her hand ever so gently on the latch. Then she would slam open the door in a rush as though she expected to find something unusual going on in the room.

The Cat's hearing, however, was exceptionally keen, and she always caught the tiny squeak in the left shoe of the Deacon's Sister. Then she would give one last lick of her tongue over her mouse-flavored lips, fling herself on her cushion, and close her eyes tightly. While the Sister glared at her, she would lie as limply as though she had not stirred for hours.

Monday Morning

It would have been quite safe if she had continued to eat only one mouse, but there came a Sabbath when she yielded to temptation and opportunity and caught two. Both mice were fat, for they had been well stuffed for some time with cheese. The Deacon's Cat ate the first one rapidly enough, and cleaned up every speck, but the second did not seem to taste quite so appetizing, though she kept on nosing and sampling and crunching. Time slipped by before she was aware of it, and the first thing she knew she heard the solid step of the Deacon. Still in front of her was a large portion of the second mouse.

My, what gulps she gave! When the Deacon entered

224

the room, the Cat had barely reached her cushion. Behind her on the floor something that had once belonged to a fat gray mouse was still lying. It was something long and thin, an unmistakable tail. Close by the big carved chest it was, as plain as could be.

The Deacon saw it, but he was, as I have told you, a little near-sighted. When he peered from that something to the Cat sleeping, or seeming to sleep, on her cushion, he shrugged his shoulders and thrust a disagreeable thought out of his mind.

"It is a piece of string, no doubt," he argued to himself. "My Sister must be getting careless with her sweeping." So he went on past the chest, took his seat in the great arm-chair, and began reading in the black-covered book.

Then the Cat heard the tiny squeak in the left shoe of the Deacon's Sister, and in she came. She was a little more breathless than usual, for someone had delayed her, and she had hurried, hoping to get home first. The minute she entered the room, she, too, saw that something lying on the floor beside the great chest.

Of course, it being Sunday, she would not pick it up, even though her fingers itched to do so. To pick up things from the floor she considered would be work, and the Deacon's Sister never worked on the Sabbath.

"What is that?" she asked her brother in a severe tone.

"What?" he asked, putting his finger on the page, and looking everywhere but where his Sister pointed.

"That!"

"Er — why, it looks like a piece of string, doesn't it?" Then the Deacon added truthfully, "I haven't really examined it."

"And how could a piece of string get in here?"

"Perhaps you forgot to sweep it out yesterday."

"That is impossible," said the Sister, snapping her mouth shut and staring at the Cat. That poor creature yawned, and wondered how soon she could leave the room safely. She did not like the subject of the conversation at all.

Nothing more was said about that something on the floor. The Cat finally marched deliberately past the Deacon's Sister, holding her head and her tail high, and slipped through the cat hole cut in the doorway. She spent the rest of the afternoon curled on top of her favorite haycock down in the river meadow, digesting two fat mice, minus one tail.

She would not have dozed so comfortably that afternoon, or dreamed so peacefully that night, had she known what the Deacon's Sister was planning.

Indeed, if the Cat had only been clever, she would have slipped back through the cat hole, while the Deacon and his Sister were sleeping, and removed the tail, which was still lying on the floor by the great chest.

However, the Cat never thought of it. It was still very early on Monday morning when the Deacon's Sister rose from her bed. As soon as she was dressed she hurried straight to the great chest and bent over the curious thing on the floor which the Deacon had suggested might be a piece of string. She lifted it cautiously between two bony fingertips. Then she shrieked and she shrieked.

The Deacon leaped from his bed, thinking Indians must be upon them. Seizing his musket, he rushed bravely toward the sound of the shrieks, clad in his long white nightgown, his nightcap sailing behind him.

There stood his Sister, still shrieking and still holding triumphantly between two fingers that long, thin tail of a mouse.

Just then the Cat came slipping through the cat hole, and the three stood looking at each other.

"That Cat caught a mouse on the Sabbath Day," said the Sister, shaking the tail in front of the Cat and then in front of the Deacon. "I have suspected as much!"

"Did you, Pussy?" asked the Deacon sternly. "Did you catch a mouse on the Sabbath in spite of what I told you?"

"M-e-o-w," said the Cat miserably. "M-e-o-w!"

"I would not have believed it of her," said the Deacon. "I can hardly believe it even now."

"Here is the proof," triumphed the Deacon's Sister, again shaking the tail between her bony fingers.

Yes, there it was. There was no denying that. The Deacon's Sister looked at it. The Deacon looked at it. The Cat looked at it.

The Deacon's Sister broke the silence. Her voice blared like Gabriel's trumpet in her brother's ears. "Remember," it thundered, "you are a Deacon, and must uphold the morals of Massachusetts."

228

"The morals even of the cats, you think, Sister?" asked the Deacon fearfully.

"Even of the cats," answered his Sister with no hesitation.

The Deacon squared his shoulders. He realized how great the crime had been and he wanted to do his duty. "A good thrashing — " he began.

"Hanging," corrected his Sister. "The mouse was murdered. There is nothing to do but hang the murderer!"

"But really!" protested the Deacon.

"Hang the Cat!" demanded the Sister. "Hang it at once." Then she added pointedly, "I should really hate to refer this affair to the other deacons."

It is well, perhaps, not to go further into details. But the result of the matter was that, much against the Deacon's will, and certainly against the Cat's, the Cat that ate the mouse on the Sabbath Day in the Province of Massachusetts, having had the offense proved against her, was taken out behind the barn to be hanged that Monday morning.

Just between us, let it be added that the string the Deacon took to hang the Cat was not very strong. Perhaps that was why the Deacon chose it. And something remarkably like a Cat was seen shortly thereafter scooting up the road faster than cats usually run.

From that day on, the Deacon's Cat was seen no more in the neighborhood. And the mice worried the Deacon's Sister until she grew more bony than ever.

Catherine Cate Coblentz

THE WILDERNESS COW

Vermont, 1789

Five little girls and their father and mother,
Two tired oxen, the old mare Bess,
Come trudging along through the wintry forest
To found a new home in the wilderness.

Bright and Star are weary with travel,
So Father must take his turn at the yoke,
And five little girls tumble out of the slow sledge
And help Father pull as a 'kind of joke.

Slowly the sledge creaks through the forest
With Bess in the lead, and the man and the ox
Pulling together and panting and straining,
Hauling the sledge through the stumps and the rocks.

But the five little girls are cheerful and laughing,
The five little girls like squirrels are merry,
And they frisk in the ruts and stumble in snowdrifts
With their eyes bright as glass and their cheeks like a berry.

And at night, by the hearth of some settler's fire,
They eat their corn meal with a big wooden spoon,
And then roll in bear-skins, their feet to the faggots,
Their heads on the floor, and so fall asleep soon.

To pay for new land, Star and Bright must be given,
And the old mare too — now they have not one beast,
But Father has fifty unbroken wild acres
And an ax and a hoe to begin with, at least.

So Father and Mother, with long snowshoes fastened
Over their boots, follow a trail
Among the blazed trees — through three feet of snow-
    drifts
With two little girls behind like a tail.

And three littlest girls crowd to a window
Of the nearest neighbor and wave and wave
Till Father and Mother and Anna and Mercy
Disappear in the forest, as dark as a cave.

When Father has built them a sheltering cabin
He returns once again to take home on his back
Little Rebecca all bundled in mufflers,
Delighted to find herself turned to a pack.

And another cold day Bethiah is carried
Through the dark woods, and Martha's brought last,
And now five little girls are once more together
Under one roof with the hard journey past.

The corn meal is gone — there's no bread to be eaten.
But luckily Father has met in the wood
An Indian brave with a moose, which he sells him,
And the children discover that moosemeat is good.

So Anna and Mercy, Rebecca, Bethiah,
And Martha — so little she looks like a mouse —
All live in the forest like five little elf-girls,
Helping their father and mother keep house.

But they do need a cow. If they only had milk now
To fill up the mugs Father carried from home,
They'd get along finely, and little thin Martha
Dreams of a milk-pail all tossing with foam.

They must have a cow, but all Father's money
Has been spent in bringing them here so far.
Still they must have a cow, but the wilderness stretches
About them in forests where no cows are.

But they hear of a merchant who is said to want sweet
flag.
Now the snowdrifts are gone, they can search all the
ground,
And Anna and Mercy with sharp eyes down-glancing
Show Father the places where the root may be found.

And Father and Mercy and Anna together
Heap up a horse-load to dry in the sun.
And then Father must carry it all to the merchant
In the far-away town when the drying is done.

"What's this?" asks the merchant. "I do not want sweet
    flag.
I never said sweet flag, no, no, sir, I vow."
And Father stands thinking of his wife and five children
All waiting so eagerly for the new cow.

And he says, "Sir, at home my five little daughters
Are watching the window to see what I bring.
Anna is ten, she has dug like a woodchuck,
And Mercy has worked just as hard all the spring.

"And even Rebecca, who's six, has been helping.
And Bethiah, who's five, has taken her share.
And four-year-old Martha has helped spread the sweet flag,
And turned it and dried it — the root I have there.

"I have only an ax and a hoe to begin with,
But I've never lost heart, as I'm losing it now.
It's more than I think my courage will carry,
To go home to my girls without leading a cow."

And the merchant said, "Hum," and coughed with emo-
tion.
And the merchant said, "Well, now," and then, "Let me
see,
I might find some use for a horse-load of sweet flag,
And I've got a young cow that is small use to me."

So next evening when Martha kept watch at the window —
It was late May and evenings were gentle and long —
She suddenly cried out, "Look! Father is coming!"
And the five little girls ran out in a throng.

"And he's brought home a cow! Oh, Mother, how
lovely!
A real, real live cow, and she's ours for to keep!"
And they clapped their hands madly and danced in a
circle,
And they each had their milk ere they fell fast asleep.

And the trees of the forest whispered together,
Saying, "Five little girls, and they're all happy now.
We are the Wilderness, stern and indifferent,
But we had to let five little girls have their cow."

Elizabeth Coatsworth

THE wind howled loudly around the little log cabin and roared down the chimney. Prudence reached out her hand and pulled the homespun woolen covers up until they nearly covered her dark curly head. It was early morning. Gray light was streaking through the tiny frost-covered windows near the rafters of the loft where the children of the Fuller family slept.

Usually Prudence was awakened by the crackling of the huge fire her father had built in the fireplace, but this morning the house was cold and still.

"Why should it be?" she wondered. Then she remembered. Yesterday they had all watched Father ride away on old Nellie's back with bags of corn and wheat hanging from the saddle. It was a two-day trip to and from the mill where the corn and wheat would be ground into corn meal and flour.

"Mother was up late last night keeping hot goose grease on Benjamin's sore throat," thought Prudence. "She must be tired. I'll hurry down and make the fire myself and surprise her."

The corn-husk mattress crackled and the rope springs squeaked as she thrust her bare feet out into the cold. She shivered as she dressed quietly in her long homespun dress. Carrying her stout leather shoes in her hand in order not to wake the others, she climbed down the ladder which led to the room below, where her mother and Baby Peregrine were asleep. It was a large square room, crudely furnished with hand-made furniture. Hooked rugs lay on the rough hard floor. A bed stood in one corner with a cradle beside it.

Kneeling before the fireplace, Prudence carefully pushed aside the ashes with a large turkey feather as she had often seen her father do. He always left the live coals well covered during the night. From these he started the new fire each morning.

Suddenly she realized that only dead gray ashes lay on the hearth before her. The live coals had died out during the night. Fear clutched at her heart. Never before could she remember being without fire in the house.

"Mother, Mother, wake up," she called. "There are no embers on the hearth. Whatever shall we do?"

Her mother sprang up quickly.

"There's only one thing we can do," Mrs. Fuller answered. "Someone will have to walk the five miles to neighbor Luce's and bring back some live coals."

"I'll go, Mother," spoke up Benjamin, a tall, serious lad of thirteen, who had just come down the ladder.

"No, Benjamin! It will be several days before your throat is well enough for you to leave the house."

"Oh, Mother!" Prudence begged. "May I go?"

"Really, my throat is better today," said Benjamin. "I am the man of the house when Father is away, and I am the one who should go. Prudence is too young. What if something should happen to her?"

"Please, Mother, I'm nearly twelve now," put in Prudence hopefully.

"Hush, children!" commanded their mother, trying to hide her anxiety. "If Father were only here!"

Patiently the children waited for her decision, each hoping to be chosen for the exciting journey. Finally Mrs. Fuller spoke. "Prudence, I shall have to let you go."

Prudence jumped up and down with excitement. "I'm not a bit afraid," she said. "I'll walk fast and be back in no time."

"Remember, young lady," put in Benjamin, "it's five long miles each way with only a rough path to follow."

"Come, you must hurry and get started, Prudence,"

said her mother. "It will be hard enough for us to keep warm until your return."

Extra warm petticoats, skirts, and shawls were piled onto Prudence until she was nearly as broad as she was tall.

"Mrs. Luce won't know who I am, Mother, I am so bundled up," the girl protested, laughing.

"Here, you might as well wear this, since I can't go," said Benjamin, handing her his cherished new woolen muffler.

Lifting an iron pot from the swinging hook in the broad fireplace, Mrs. Fuller handed it to Prudence.

"Fill this pot with as many embers as Mrs. Luce can spare, and let nothing happen to them on the way home," she directed. She put a covered pewter dish into the pot. "This is fresh goose grease and may come in handy for Mrs. Luce. We are going to have a hard winter if today is a sample."

As Prudence kissed her mother good-by, she noticed the worried look on Mrs. Fuller's face. "You shouldn't feel badly about my going, Mother. It will be so much fun to see Abigail and Jerusha again. I can hardly wait."

"Well, do be careful, child, not to stray from the path," her mother warned, as she tied the strings of Prudence's warm hood snugly under her chin.

At a bend in the path the girl turned to wave good-by to her mother standing in the cabin doorway.

"Don't worry. I'll be safe," she called gaily.

The trees were thick and uncut for miles around, except for the few clearings like their own. These were grants of land given by the Government to the men who returned from fighting in the Revolutionary War.

Humming a merry tune, Prudence skipped along the path as fast as her heavy clothing would permit. At first the woodland was familiar and she passed places where she had been many times before. There was a thicket where she and Benjamin had picked huckleberries some weeks earlier. Prudence remembered how pleased Mother had looked when she saw them. Even Father had said it would be good to taste one of Mother's huckleberry pies again.

As the girl walked along, a cold wind whistled past. It nipped her nose and made her fingers so numb she could hardly hold on to the handle of the iron pot.

"This will never do," she thought. "I'll have to get warmer somehow."

After setting the pot down, she pulled off her mittens, cupped her hands before her mouth, and breathed her warm breath on her stiff red fingers until she could bend them once more. Then she pulled Benjamin's warm muffler up over her cold nose. "There, that's better," she thought, and started on over the rough path.

Presently she came to a halt. Before her was a fork in the road. One path led straight ahead and the other bore to the left into the deep forest. For an instant she was frightened.

"Oh, which way shall I go?" she thought wildly. "I never knew that there were two paths between here and Abigail's."

She half turned to go back. Then the thought of the cold cabin at home gave her courage. She looked about her carefully.

"The path straight ahead looks the most traveled to me," she said to herself. "I'm going to follow that one. Oh, I do hope it will take me to Luces'!" she added anxiously.

After a long time she came upon a clearing, in the center of which stood a log cabin much like her own.

"Thank goodness!" she exclaimed. "That was the right path because there's Abigail's home." A thin curl of blue smoke was coming out of the chimney. The thought of a fire made her feet fairly fly to the cabin door. As she knocked, two bright-faced girls appeared at the door.

"Oh, Prudence," the older one cried, "how did you happen to come? Are you all alone? Can you stay a while?"

"We have no fire at home," Prudence answered. "I have come to carry back some embers if you can spare them."

"Oh, Mother, we haven't seen Prudence in weeks and weeks! Can't she stay awhile?" begged the younger girl.

"Prudence must get back to her family as soon as possible, girls, if they are without a fire this cold day," Mrs. Luce answered. "But it would be well for her to eat dinner with us and to get thoroughly warm before she sets out for home again."

So seldom did the girls see one another that they kept up a lively stream of chatter over their dinner of hominy, sirup, and venison.

After many invitations to come again, Prudence set out on the return journey. The iron pot was nearly full of precious embers and she hung on tightly to the handle as though nothing on earth could take it away from her.

Somehow the journey home seemed longer than the way she had come. The pot grew very heavy for her cold hands to carry and her muscles ached. Several times as she trudged along, she was forced to set it down to rest her weary arms.

The sky grew gray and threatening and cast dark shadows over the surrounding forest. Gradually the giant trees seemed to close in upon her and she felt very small and alone. For the first time she was really afraid.

After this she hurried along the path, ears alert, not looking to the right or left. Every noise made her start.

Later on, large, feathery snowflakes began to fall. They clung to the pine trees and made the path slippery and more difficult to walk upon. It seemed to Prudence that she had walked for many miles.

"Oh, I must hurry," she said to herself desperately. She tried to quicken her footsteps but her feet were cold and heavy. After what seemed like an endless stretch of time she came upon the fork in the road which had puzzled her so that morning.

"I am not so far from home now," she said to herself with relief and new courage.

The quiet of the forest was suddenly broken by a sharp crackling sound in the bushes behind her. What could it be? She turned about with a jerk. But she could see nothing unusual.

She walked on for a short distance. The crackling sounded again, nearer.

Turning once more, she stood paralyzed with fright. Only her eyes moved as she looked in the direction of the sound. A short distance away in the shadows of the bushes, she saw an animal creeping toward her.

Immediately she knew from its long, grayish-yellow body, short legs, and small head that it was the dreaded panther whose cries they had been hearing at night. She thought of hurling the pot of embers at him. The fear of fire might frighten him away.

"No, I mustn't do that," she realized. "They need these embers too badly at home."

Suddenly there flashed through her mind some words she had heard her grandmother say: "As long as you face a panther and do not turn your back to him, he will not attack you."

Immediately she started walking backward. She walked slowly and carefully, for fear she might trip and fall.

At first the panther slowed his steps as though he had changed his mind about following, but Prudence did not falter in her steady backward walk. As moments passed, the panther drew nearer and nearer until Prudence could see his white breast and yellow eyes.

Suddenly it seemed to her that she heard a sound like hoof beats but she decided it must be the thumping of her heart.

"How much longer can I walk like this?" she thought.

At that moment she felt herself stepping on something round and slippery. Her foot turned with the stone. Desperately she tried to catch herself, but down she went.

As she tried to rise, she saw the panther crouching on all fours. It was gathering strength for a leap. Sick with terror, she covered her face with her arm. Her heart beat loudly. Again it sounded just like the clop, clop of a horse's hoofs. Then there was a sharp report, followed by an angry growl, and a dull thud near her side. Everything turned black.

When Prudence opened her bewildered eyes, she saw that she was lying in her own warm, cheerful cabin.

She started up. "Did I lose the embers?" she demanded.

Loving arms tightened around her shoulders as her mother drew her down.

"No, Prudence," said her father in a voice husky with pride, as he stood looking down at her. "You were still clutching the pot safely in your hand when old Nellie and I rode up. It did not take long for my old musket to put that panther where it can do no more harm."

"I wish I'd been there!" sighed Benjamin, boy-fashion, as he piled a huge log onto the roaring fire.

They all laughed, and even the baby gurgled.

"But I don't understand why you were walking backward," puzzled Mr. Fuller.

Prudence looked up at him in astonishment. "Didn't Grandmother ever tell you," she demanded, "that you must always face a panther?"

Sarah Elizabeth Merrill

THE PEDDLER'S CLOCK

MILES, Ezra, and Timothy Bellamy needed no clock to tell them when it was time to bring the cows home. It would have done them no good to wish for one, either, for Father was stubborn about having a clock in the house. He was jealous for the big silver watch which his own father had bought in Boston sixty years before.

Sometimes, when Father wound the watch at night, he would allow the children to hold it, careful all the while to see that no harm came to his precious heirloom. When he went off on any kind of journey, he always wore the watch, looking very grand with the thick silver chain looped across his vest. But such occasions were rare. Most of the time the watch ticked away in its bulky leather case, hidden in the top drawer of the tall desk that stood in the parlor of the Connecticut farmhouse where the Bellamys were living in 1822.

So, for the most part, the days were measured for the family by the position of the sun in the sky, by the shadows which were cast by this or that familiar object. When the sun stood, as it seemed to Timothy, about a foot from the dark line of forest that lay to the westward, he knew that it was time for him and his brothers to bring Daisy and Sukey and Mooly home for the milking.

Miles, who was the eldest, claimed Daisy for his cow. Ezra pretended that Sukey belonged to him. Mooly, a gentle creature without horns, was the pet and special charge of Timothy. Each boy milked his own cow, morning and night, and carried in the brimming pails.

Mother had been provoked with Father on the day that he had bought Mooly. "Another cow?" she exclaimed. "When Daisy and Sukey give us all the milk we need! I declare, Jonathan, you are foolish over cows. I would much rather you had bought us a clock."

But Father said, "We have one perfectly good timepiece in the house. That is enough. And a cow is valuable property, whereas a clock is just an ornament!"

"Tush, Jonathan," said Grandmother Bellamy. "You exaggerate to suit your own argument. A clock is certainly more than an ornament, and Elizabeth wouldn't want just the works of a clock without any case, such as folks call a 'wag-on-the-wall.' "

"No," said Mother, "I want a clock in a nice case with pictures painted on the glass."

Mother's eyes shone a little, as if she could plainly see the clock of her dreams.

"That's a frivolous wish, Elizabeth," reproved Father, "and not in keeping with your good judgment. Clocks are expensive luxuries, and I can ill afford to buy one."

"But, Father," said seventeen-year-old Penelope, timidly, "these new shelf-clocks with wooden works are much less dear."

"A clock would be company," murmured Mother. At that everyone had to laugh, for Mother certainly never lacked for company, with the house full of young ones.

" 'Lay not up for yourselves treasures upon earth,' " said Father. Surely a quotation from the Bible would put a stop to all arguments!

There were twinkles in Grandmother's eyes, as she said slyly, "What about thy silver watch, Jonathan?"

Only Grandmother dared to talk back to Father. For though he was kind, he was also stern, and the lord and master of his household, as fathers were in those days.

So Mother continued to do without a clock, and Mooly, the cow, stayed on the farm.

TEMPTATION

One summer morning a few weeks later, Father, dressed in his best, with his silver watch in his pocket, set off very early for Colchester on a matter of business. He wanted to attend a public meeting as well, and planned to stay the night with one of his relatives. It always seemed strange on the farm without Father. The days were longer than ordinary days, and the nights more still and lonely.

Toward evening of this day, when the milking had been done and Mother had supper almost ready, there came the sound of hoofs in the lane, and of someone hallooing outside. Everyone crowded to the door. A tall, lean fellow was alighting from his horse.

"A peddler, I think," said Mother.

"Good day to you, Mistress," said the peddler, with a quick, stiff bow. "And to all that dwell in the house," he added, looking at the children with a little twinkling smile.

He took his pack off the horse. He laid it down on the grass of the dooryard. Carefully he drew out something and unwound the wrappings. There was a clock!

Up to the door he marched, carrying the clock. Mother backed away a little, as if she knew that here was Temptation with a capital T.

"I represent Ebenezer Plumb, clockmaker, silversmith, and bell-caster of Wethersfield," said the peddler. "I am almost at my journey's end. I have sold every buckle, every candlestick, every spoon, every clock that I had when setting forth from the shop a week ago. All, good Mistress, but this shelf-clock and three cowbells. What will you offer for this fine clock, the best of the lot?"

He laid the clock in Mother's arms. As she looked down at it, a little smile played about her lips. It was the clock of her dreams. It was in a cherry case, smoothly polished and beautifully carved, with a graceful scroll at the top. There were slender pillars at the sides, topped by balls.

248

Little pink rosebuds were painted on the face, and a wreath of full-blown roses bloomed on the glass door. It seemed as if the hands that pointed the hours must have been hammered in a fairy forge by fairy fingers, so delicately were they carved.

"Just set it up in the house somewhere," said the peddler, "and I will start it going and let you hear how it sounds when it strikes the hour."

Mother could not resist this suggestion. She stood it up on the dresser in the kitchen. And presently the wooden pendulum, overlaid with brass, was swinging back and forth, gleaming within the circle of roses.

"Now," said the peddler, "when the minute hand points exactly to figure twelve, and the hour hand exactly to five, the clock will strike the hour."

Timothy held his breath, waiting, while the minute hand moved, second by second. And sure enough, when it pointed to figure twelve, there fell upon the listening ears five cheerful notes. Everyone, including the peddler, looked at Mother. She stood, with clasped hands, gazing at the clock. Her cheeks were pink, her eyes bright.

"Well," said the peddler, "will you buy the clock?"

"Alas," sighed Mother, "I have no money, and my husband is not at home." She turned her back to the clock and looked at the peddler with tragic eyes. "You had best go," she said. It really made one feel dreadfully sorry to see Mother giving up the beautiful clock.

"Oh, Mother," cried Penelope, "maybe the man would trade something for the clock."

"I might consider it," said the peddler. "What have you to trade?"

Mother looked at Penelope. She looked at Grandmother. She held a corner of her apron to her mouth, thinking. Then she threw up her chin. She spoke breathlessly, "I have a cow!"

"Elizabeth!" gasped Grandmother.

"Mother!" cried Penelope.

"Mother! Which cow?" Timothy's voice was a frightened squeak.

But Mother looked straight at the peddler. "Are you interested in such a trade?" she asked.

"If it is a good cow," answered the peddler.

"We have only good cows," said Mother. "Come. You may see for yourself." She led the way to the barn and Timothy trotted after her. Ezra started, too, and one of the girls. But Mother turned swiftly. "Go back into the house, children," she said. "This bargain is between the peddler and me."

Timothy stood at the window, his heart almost bursting with anxiety. He caught his breath as Mother and the peddler came out of the barn. The peddler was leading Mooly!

"Oh-h-h, Grandmother," moaned Timothy, "he's taking my cow!"

Grandmother seized him just as he was dashing out of the door. "Timothy! You are not to say a word. Mooly is not really your cow. And your mother is doing what she thinks best. At least, she is doing what she wants to."

And there was the peddler going off down the lane, the horse's rein in one hand, and the rope which led Mooly in the other.

"Now we'll have supper," said Mother.

"How can she be so calm?" thought Timothy.

Off he dashed after the peddler, who heard the boy's shouts and drew rein. Timothy looked up, breathless. "You don't even know her name!" he cried. "It's Mooly."

"I might have guessed that," laughed the peddler, "since she hasn't any horns. That's one reason I wanted her."

Timothy dug his bare toes in the dust of the road. "You will be good to her, won't you?"

"She'll be Ebenezer Plumb's cow, not mine, boy. But never fear, the master will be good to her. I must be getting on now."

"Let me pet her just once," cried Timothy. He leaned against the cow, stroking her neck. "Good-by, Mooly," he whispered.

"I guess you feel sort of bad to see her go," said the peddler. "Here, I'll give you a present." He fished into his pack and pulled out the three cowbells.

"Much obliged," said Timothy, jingling the bells. And for a moment he felt a warm glow of happiness from the unexpected gift. But as the peddler disappeared at a bend in the road, the thought came to Timothy, "Three cowbells, but only two cows!"

Rainbow in the Sky

Still, the evening seemed gay. To have the new clock there on the dresser was like having a cheerful and honored guest in the house. The eyes of everyone were constantly turning to it, watching the minute hand as it traveled round and round, and the slow creep of the hour hand. The shine of the polished case, the golden gleam of the swinging pendulum, the dainty pink of the painted roses gave an air of luxury to the big plain kitchen. And as the hours of six, and seven, and eight were told, all were silent, giving ear to the measured notes that filled the room with a music sweeter far than that of Ezra's jew's-harp.

But the next morning there was no Mooly to milk, and Timothy felt lost. As the day wore on, and the hour of Father's return drew nearer, an atmosphere of strain became evident among the Bellamys. They stole looks at each other, and at Mother's straight mouth.

It was late afternoon when Father returned. He was happy to be at home again. He put his watch carefully away in its case, changed his clothes, and they all sat down to supper in the kitchen.

"There isn't anyone can cook like you, Elizabeth," he said. He was just on the point of taking a great bite of food when the clock struck six. He lowered his fork quickly. "What's that?" he demanded.

"That's the new clock, Jonathan," said Grandmother in her most soothing tone. "Doesn't it sound nice?"

Miles gave a small excited giggle.

Father looked at the clock, frowning. "Where did it come from?"

"I got it from a peddler," answered Mother, "representing Ebenezer Plumb of Wethersfield."

"And what, may I ask, did you give him for it?" asked Father, coldly.

"One of the cows," said Mother. "Mooly."

Father pushed back his chair, and stared at Mother. "You mean you traded Mooly for that fancy creation yonder?"

"Yes," said Mother.

Father's face was like a thundercloud. He stood up. "I won't say what I think before the children," he said. He strode out of the house, walking to the barn with long rapid steps.

It was an unhappy evening. Everyone went to bed very early.

The next morning was rainy. At breakfast Father said

pointedly, "Since there is no cow for you to milk, Timothy, you may come and help me grease axles."

In the barn Timothy said, "Father, I thought it was a terrible piece of bargaining, too. The cow's worth lots more than the clock."

Father coughed. "You must never criticize your mother, Timothy."

"No, Father," answered Timothy. "I do think the clock is nice. But, Father, I want to tell you. Last night, in bed, I planned how we can get Mooly back. I could go and be an apprentice to Ebenezer Plumb and work out the price of Mooly."

"That would take a long time, son," said Father. "And you were never cut out for a craftsman. You're a born farmer, like your father." He gave Timothy a look that made the boy's heart beat high with happiness.

They worked in silence for a few moments. Then Father spoke again. "Son, run to the house and bring me a gourdful of soft soap and my coat and hat."

After Father had washed his hands at the trough and put on his coat and hat, he saddled his horse. "Now, Timothy, I'm going away. You can say that I shall be back by evening." And Father was off, in the rain.

All day Timothy wondered where Father had gone. Mother looked pale and unhappy, for there had been never a word of farewell.

The new bells that Daisy and Sukey wore made a pleasant jangle as they came across the pasture and into the barnyard that evening. The clouds had broken in the west. There was a rainbow in the sky. Timothy was standing in the barn doorway watching it, while his brothers did the milking, when, suddenly, there was Father with Mooly.

"Here, Timothy," he said, "here's your cow! Take her into her stall, where she belongs."

"Father!" cried Timothy, his face shining with joy. "How did you get her back?"

"I went to the clockmaker's shop and paid him what the clock was worth."

Father ate a hearty supper that evening. He got up from the table and stretched himself. "Ho-hum!" he yawned. Then he said, "That's a handsome clock, Elizabeth, mighty handsome! Come winter, and I will make you a nice shelf for it. How would you like that?"

"I'd like it very much, Jonathan."

Mother and Father smiled at each other. Suddenly it seemed as if the whole house were filled with sunshine. The children began to laugh and chatter, and Grandmother's face was lit with a quiet happiness.

Timothy was happiest of all. He took the pail and ran out to the barn. First he tied the extra bell around Mooly's neck. "Three bells — three cows," he said. He sat down on the milking-stool and pressed his head against Mooly's smooth flank. The sound of the milk hissing against the sides of the pail was sweeter to Timothy's ears than the golden chimes of any clock could ever be.

Mabel Leigh Hunt

ANGEL ON SKIS

M UMMIE, Mummie, come quick! The man's flying!
Hurry, Mummie!"

The little boy's voice was shrill with excitement and
wonder. Mrs. Stacey ran out of the door of the shack,

her heart beating with hope. The thought of a man coming flying, as Bobbie put it, made her smile happily to herself. He could not come too soon. Daddy must have sent him up from Oroville with their sorely needed supplies. What luck!

As the thoughts tumbled through her mind, she reached her son's side on the ridge that rose, bare of trees, just back of the dwelling.

"Look!" He pointed an eager hand.

Clear against the blue sky, the figure of a man was outlined, speeding down the distant, snow-covered slope. The descent made Mrs. Stacey think of the swoop of an eagle rather than of anything possible to a human being. She gasped, staring. The figure swung downward in long loops, disappeared for a moment behind a mass of rock, appeared once again, turned, and vanished over the further side of the mountain.

Mother and son looked at each other. The boy's eyes were brilliant with wonder. His pale cheeks were flushed pink.

"Was it an angel, Mummie? He didn't have wings."

"No, he isn't a real angel, of course, and what wings he has are on his feet, not his shoulders, but he's a good man and kind. I think he must be the man folks call 'Snowshoe Thompson,' or sometimes the 'Angel on Skis.'"

"I wish he'd been coming here, not going away, Mummie."

Struggling against the disappointment that had swept over her when she realized that the flying man was not a rescuer sent to bring Bobbie and herself to safety, Mrs. Stacey managed a smile.

"Come in and help me build up the fire, son, and I'll tell you about him."

After the two had brought in wood from the lean-to and mended the fire, the mother seated herself in a chair made of wood and deer-hides, and pulled her six-year-old youngster into her lap. For a moment she gazed into the flames, her thoughts following down the long trail Jim had taken to Oroville. Thirty miles and more it was, through all this snow. That was a hard trip for a man still weak after illness.

"Begin, Mummie, please." The little boy turned his head to look up into her face.

"Yes, of course. Snowshoe Thompson. It really isn't snowshoes he uses, but things he calls 'skis.' He came from Norway, a country far away, where the people use these things through their snow-buried winters. The skis are long, narrow boards, pointed, and they tip up a little in front. Straps hold them on. The Norwegians learn to travel on their skis from the time they're small boys, no older than you. And when they are grown men, well, you saw what they can do. And that's only a part. Your Daddy said Mr. Thompson can jump right off a cliff or clear over a creek, sailing through the air like a great bird, or like an angel. That's one reason they nicknamed him 'Angel on Skis.' Besides, he seems like an angel to the men in the gold camps. Some of them, you know, never see a soul, once the winter sets in. They get no papers or letters, no word from the rest of the world. Sometimes they fall sick, and sometimes they even die, way out in some little claim, like this one of ours."

Her voice sank with the last words, and she caught her breath.

"Many times Snowshoe Thompson comes flying in, with his pack on his back, bringing them word of those they love back home. He brings them all the news of the gold camps, as well as of Sacramento and San Francisco, and carries medicines, too. If he finds anyone really ill, he makes a sled and pulls the sick man to Placerville or some settlement where there's a doctor. If it is food the person needs, he sees that it gets to him. He moves fast on those skis of his. In a few hours he can cover ground it would take days for a man to travel on foot or on snowshoes. Your father said that there's no other man the country over that travels so fast as Snowshoe Thompson."

"I wish I had skis. I'd go flying, too."

Mrs. Stacey laughed, the first laugh in quite a long while that she had not forced.

"Daddy told me that several of the men have tried to learn to use skis, too. He said they just turned pinwheels, and one came near breaking his leg. Mr. Thompson says that if they'd take time they could learn, but Daddy thinks probably anybody has to start young. Well, I must see about getting something for us to eat now."

"I wish Daddy would come back. It's almost Christmas, and he said he'd bring me a present and you one, too. And maybe something to eat that isn't just mush and salt pork."

260

"It's a long, long way to Oroville, darling, and then just as far back again. You must be patient. But what a feast we'll have when Daddy gets back with a big sled full of Christmas gifts and good things to eat. We'll just pretend we are going to have some right now. What shall it be, Bobbie? Roast chicken and mashed potatoes and — "

He interrupted her, laughing. "And pie and cranberry sauce and hot cakes and sirup and plum cake and — and oh, everything good!"

But it was difficult to pretend that the mush was anything but mush, and that the salt pork tasted like roast chicken. A feeling of fear ran through Mrs. Stacey when she noticed how very little pork or meal remained.

This was the sixth day since Jim had gone. He had hoped to get down to Oroville in two or three days at the longest, and surely men could get up to her cabin in another two, even though it had snowed again. She was eating as little as possible, but she dared not let herself get too weak, for if she should give out, what would become of Bobbie?

When the meal, helped down with hot tea, was over, Mrs. Stacey sent her boy out to play while the sun was warm, and sank, exhausted, in her chair. She knew she must save every ounce of her strength.

"It can't be much longer," she told herself. "It can't."

The Staceys had not meant to be caught here by winter. Five weeks ago, before the first snow had fallen, Jim had gone to Oroville to bank the gold dust he had washed out of his claim, by working all spring and summer. It had been a lucky little claim, bringing in much more than he had dared hope for. There was enough to start the store he planned to set up in Sacramento, and with what he could sell the claim for, enough to build them a little home. He came back from Oroville, whistling, happy, bringing a burro that would carry their pack and Bobbie too.

Then, as though struck by lightning, he had fallen ill, terribly ill, with high fever, a cough, and pains all over his body. In a week his strength was gone. He could not even sit up in bed. But a turn for the better had come and he had begun to mend slowly. Before he was strong enough to take more than a few steps, however, the first real snow had come, earlier than usual. The burro, which they had let loose to find food for itself because they had none for it, wandered off. Probably it had died in some snow-drift. Their own stores began to grow scarce.

One evening Jim had glanced up from the pair of home-made snowshoes he was shaping from strips of rawhide and spruce branches.

"I've got to get down to Oroville, Mary," he had said. "There's no use hanging on here longer."

"You aren't strong enough yet, Jim," she had insisted. "You must wait a bit longer."

He had shaken his head. "I'm going tomorrow morning, just the same. The winter won't get better, nor the food last out another week."

She had watched him go, with a pack on his back containing a blanket and what food could be spared. He had barely enough food for three days. Had he known how little remained, she could not have persuaded him to take that much. He had insisted on leaving his gun with her.

"Something might happen to make you need it. Maybe, too, you could shoot a squirrel, and you and Bobbie could have a real feast," he had told her, as he kissed her good-by. "Keep up your courage, Mary, my girl, and don't fret about me."

"Hello, Snowshoe, old-timer. Good to see you again!"

The cheerful greetings rang out as Snowshoe Thompson, two days after Bobbie had caught sight of his speeding figure, came swinging into Oroville. He was a golden-haired, blue-eyed giant, with a huge pack on his back, and a broad smile on his face.

"Merry Christmas, my friends. She soon come now, and I bring you plenty letters from your sweethearts. You glad to see me, so? And I, I hope you all got plenty nice new shining gold, to make you happy."

There was a general laugh. The skier had stopped before the two-story hotel, throwing his pack on the floor, slipping off his skis. The men and the few women who had stayed for the winter crowded about him, full of questions. How was so-and-so, had he seen this one's wife, another's mother or sister? Was his ranch in Carson buried under snow? What was the political news from Sacramento?

"Last I heard," one man announced, "they were talking of building a railroad across the Sierras and over the plains to Independence. They're sure plumb crazy in that town."

"They'll build it, crazy or not. Who isn't crazy in this part of the world?"

Thompson opened his pack and began to haul out letters and papers and a few parcels, calling out names and handing what he had to those who stepped forward. There were four or five children in the camp, and Snowshoe had remembered them with a small toy for each. Laughter, thanks, exclamations came from those who began to read their mail. It was a scene good to witness.

That evening, over supper, at a round table where his particular friends were seated with him, Thompson told some of the adventures he had met on the long trip from the Nevada border, where his ranch lay. He described how he had zigzagged from one lonely claim to another, to small camps and isolated cabins. The early snow had brought hardships.

"Say," inquired Grant, the proprietor of the hotel, "how about young Stacey and his wife and kid up on South Fork? Did they get out before the snow came?"

"Sure," another man answered. "Stacey was here to ship his dust through to San Francisco by Wells Fargo about the middle of November. He told me he was taking a burro back and would pull out in the next two-three days. That young fellow struck it rich, and was all set to start a general store in Sacramento. Felt pretty good, he did."

"Sure they got out, Wilkins?" asked Grant, turning to the speaker. "I don't recall seeing them go through."

"Lot of folk pulling out about that time. Stacey told me he was all ready to leave, and he sure wouldn't sit round waiting for the snow to catch him."

"No sense doing that," Snowshoe agreed. "And the snow didn't come for a good two weeks and more after that."

Thompson stayed over the next day, visiting around a bit, taking it easy before the run down the Feather River from Oroville to Marysville. He had about finished with this particular trip, and intended to spend Christmas with an old friend in Marysville. So, early in the morning of the twenty-third of December, having breakfasted with the Grants, he came out with his host to the veranda to put on his skis. It was a brilliant day, cold and bracing. The snow was in prime condition and the skiing would be perfect. His pack was light — only the few letters he was taking down from Oroville and his own light baggage.

"Hate to have you go, Thompson. It's a grand thing to have you come, I can tell you. You don't know how much it meant to the wife to get that Christmas package from her folks, and — " he stopped, turning his head to glance up the winding road, attracted by a shout. A man was running down toward them, waving his arms.

"Hello, what's doing?"

Panting, the man arrived and climbed the steps.

"Snowshoe," he gasped, "I'm glad I caught you. Two men have brought Stacey in, nearly dead. He can't talk sense, just mumbles. No signs of his wife and kid. Either they're lost in the snow, or he left them up at his claim. Maybe they've starved to death."

"Stacey? The man on South Fork they told me got out in November?" Snowshoe turned to Grant. "You pack a sled with food, canned milk, you know what, and I'll go up right away. Now I'll go see this Stacey. Maybe he can talk better soon."

"I'll see to the sled, Thompson. You take him to Stacey, George. It sure is luck you got here in time. Ten minutes later and Snowshoe would have been several miles away."

Thompson found young Stacey in bed, being cared for by the wife of one of the men who had found him.

"They found him in a deserted log cabin," she told Thompson. "One of his snowshoes was lost, and he was huddled in a corner. My husband began rubbing him, and he opened his eyes. He started mumbling, but they couldn't make sense out of what he said. But just now he whispered to me, 'Get Mary and Bobbie — my cabin,' and then he lay quiet, just as he is now."

Snowshoe looked him over. He had had plenty of experience with starved and half-frozen men. So, too, had the woman tending him. She nodded when Thompson said, folding back the blankets in which Stacey was wrapped, "He'll come out all right. You tell him, soon as he can understand, that Snowshoe Thompson will take care of his wife and the boy. Please God I find them safe."

A half hour later the skier was on his way, dragging a narrow sled by straps harnessed to shoulders and waist. It was loaded with canned food and milk, a chicken, a ham, eggs, bread, and butter. Oroville's citizens had brought of their best, and far more than Snowshoe could take or would need. One woman even brought a cake.

"It'll be a Christmas gift for the little boy," she said.

CHRISTMAS IN THE CABIN

The trail was a tough one, almost steadily uphill, and Thompson had to depend to a large extent on the snowshoes he always carried with him. But there were stretches where he could go full speed on his skis. The dark caught him early, but he kept on until he was fearful of missing the blazes on the trees, marking the trail. Then he stopped for the night.

Digging out a hole in the lee of a thicket of young spruce, he built a fire in front. After a brief supper of sandwiches and coffee, he rolled up in his double woolen blanket to sleep. Before dawn he was on his way. He reached the cabin in the afternoon, after a stiff climb of several miles.

The shack stood on the further side of a small plateau. Slipping on his skis, Snowshoe sped across the space. He felt uneasy as he noticed that no smoke was coming from the tin smokestack. Nor was anyone stirring as he reached the door, and knocked heavily upon it. Was he too late?

A thin, trembling voice called out, "Daddy, Daddy," and a child opened the door. But when Bobbie saw the big stranger, he shrank back and began to cry.

Snowshoe soon had him smiling, the poor little white-faced youngster. "Your Daddy sent me to bring you and your mother down to him, Sonny. Don't be scared. I've brought lots of goodies to eat, and a fine new top for you to play with. Wait till I take off my skis."

"Skis?" Bobbie's eyes lighted. "You are the Angel on Skis! I saw you — long ago, over there, but you went away." Again his eyes flooded, though he kept his smile. "I'm glad you've come," he declared, as Thompson, leaning his skis against the cabin, came in, carrying stuff from the sled and looking anxiously for Mrs. Stacey. "I was lonesome. Mummie won't wake up, and it's cold, and I'm hungry. I only had a little cold mush today."

"Where's Mummie?"

"She's on the bed in the little room. Come."

Grasping Snowshoe by the hand, Bobbie led him to

269

where Mary lay, still and white, on her bed. She was unconscious, but alive.

In a jiffy, there was a big fire blazing, and milk was warming. Snowshoe carried Mary into the big room and laid her on the home-made couch. Then he knelt by her side with a cup of hot milk and fed her with a small spoon after she had opened her eyes. Placing her head gently back on the rolled blanket that did for a pillow, Snowshoe smiled at Bobbie.

"We'll give your Mummie some more milk soon, with nice beaten egg in it, Sonny. And now you and I'll have dinner. You feeling pretty fine?"

"Yes. Did you say you brought me a top?" A slightly

anxious note in the child's voice made Thompson grin even more broadly.

"By and by we'll see about that top."

They had scrambled eggs and buttered toast and hot sweet milk and a slice of ham. Snowshoe made Bobbie eat very slowly.

Every now and then, Snowshoe got up to give Mrs. Stacey more milk, and presently she was sitting up against the rolled blanket. Snowshoe told her about her husband, how he was being taken care of and would be all right. The man had a slow, pleasant voice and a friendly way.

"What day is it?" Mary asked, as her strength came back and she was allowed a little solid food.

"Christmas Eve, Mrs. Stacey. Tomorrow we'll have roast chicken and a fine cake and canned peas and cranberry sauce and potato. How about that, Bobbie?"

"Um," said Bobbie, who was feeling very sleepy, very comfortable. It was so good to be warm and full of food, and to hear Mummie talking again.

The next thing Bobbie knew he woke up in his small bed, and the sun was shining in through the two windows. His mother was sitting, wrapped in a comforter, beside the fire, eating a poached egg and drinking coffee. She smiled at him. "Merry Christmas, Bobbie."

He tumbled out of bed and ran to hug her. "Where's the big man, Mummie? Where's the Angel?"

"He's out in the shed, getting wood. Bobbie, how you've slept!"

"I'm hungry."

"We'll soon see to that," said Snowshoe, coming in with a great armful of wood.

"Merry Christmas," shouted Bobbie. "Where's my — "

He followed Thompson's pointing finger to where, on a small table in a corner, a large iced cake and a big red tin top stood proudly, with sprigs of green spruce making a wreath around them.

It was a grand day, a real Christmas, though Daddy ought to have been with them. But Snowshoe said he was having a good Christmas, too, and that they would all have another when they were together again in Oroville. Besides the top, which was a fine hummer, there was a box of tin soldiers. The dinner Snowshoe cooked was marvelous. Mummie ate almost as much as Bobbie, and laughed, and teased him, the way she used to, the way he loved to be teased.

The next morning, Bobbie sat in his mother's lap on the sled, with blankets around them both, and a back arranged for her to lean against. In front, the big man in his fur cap went so fast on the long boards that it was really like flying, especially when the trail straightened out on the long slopes.

"I like this better than the burro, Mummie."

"It's the finest ride you and I will ever have, Bobbie, darling."

In her heart Mary thought, holding her little son tight in her arms, "Suppose there had been no Angel on Skis!"

Hildegarde Hawthorne

ANIMALS
BRAVE AND WISE

SONG OF THE SHIP'S CAT

To stretch asleep
On the deck in the sun
Or to doze
In a sail that's furled,
And at night to make
The gray rats run —
That's the way
To see the world!
If you're a cat
Of spirit and sense
That's the way
To see the world!

The waves lie far
Below the rail,
The galley door
Lies near.
There's always a shadow
From the sail

If the sun shines
Too hot and clear.
For a cat who knows
His way on this earth
The good things
Always lie near.

The smell of new ports
Where a cat can rove,
And the sights
Are strange as may be.
What tales I shall have
To tell by the stove
When I am too old
For the sea!
For a cat who retires
When whiskers turn gray
Should bring back fine tales
From the sea!

Elizabeth Coatsworth

THE SEAFARING CAT

ON rainy Saturday mornings, the best place in Salem was Mr. Ezra Haskins's sail loft. That was what Patty Raeburn thought, as she and brother Dan and Grandfather walked together down the narrow street. Patty had her red cloak wrapped around her, but she had a hard time keeping it fastened, for the wind blew the warm rain all about them. At the end of the street they could see the row of wharves, the line of ships at anchor, and the water of Salem harbor, very smooth and gray under the soft shower of rain.

"Look, Grandfather," Patty was saying. "We can see both ships from here, the *Spitfire* and the *Adventure*, next to each other."

"They must be almost loaded," Dan added. "All they are waiting for is the new mainsail for each one. And Mr. Haskins says they are almost done. Patty, what are you doing?"

Patty had wheeled about suddenly and was saying, "Shoo, shoo! Go back, Tiger. This is no place for cats. Shoo!"

The little striped kitten always loved to follow people, and, though Patty had thought she was shut in the house, here she was. With her tail sticking straight up, she came galloping down the crowded street among the legs of sailors and the wheels of carts. But at Patty's order she turned around and made for home again. She had disappeared entirely by the time they got to the steps that led up to the sail loft.

The sail loft was long and low, with open rafters and a wide floor so smooth and polished that it would do for a ballroom. Here the white canvas was laid out to be cut and stitched and made into the broad white sails that carried Salem ships to the very ends of the earth a hundred years ago. Grandfather had been a captain but was too old for voyaging now. His oldest son, father of Patty and Dan, was away on a voyage that would take two years. In Salem every man, so it seemed, had been to sea or was away at sea. All the boys were only waiting for the time when they could go.

There were important visitors at the sail loft that morning. As Patty and Dan came in, Mr. Ezra Haskins was saying, "Yes, Mr. Derby, both sails will be finished before the day is out. I pledge you my word, sir."

His tone was deeply respectful, for Mr. Elias Derby was the great man of Salem. He owned many fine ships, including those two lying at the wharf, the *Adventure* and the *Spitfire*, so soon to sail for Calcutta. With Mr. Derby were two young men whom you might almost take for boys, though they were both captains of ships. Tom Raeburn, Grandfather's younger son, was one of them. Captain Samuel Horne was the other. Each was to take one of the ships to India, and they were impatient for the sails to be finished.

"You mustn't fail us, Ezra Haskins," the young man with

the yellow hair was saying. "No one wants to lose a day of this favorable weather, and I am going to make mine a record trip to India. Tom Raeburn won't mind waiting. If any sail is delayed, let it be his."

His voice was joking, but Patty saw that it was no joke to tall Tom Raeburn, whose brown cheeks grew red with excitement.

"So I don't mind waiting!" Raeburn almost shouted. "Don't forget that I have sailed a year longer than you, Sam Horne. And the *Adventure* and I are going to make a quicker voyage to India than you, I have promised myself that. You all say I sail too carefully, but I will show that I can sail swiftly, too. I allow myself a hundred days to Calcutta, a hundred days lying there to get a cargo and to load it, a hundred days to return. We will be back in Salem within the year, and few ships have bettered that."

"The *Spitfire* will better it," Sam Horne returned hotly. "We will do it under a hundred days for each voyage, and be anchored in Salem harbor before you even lift land."

"Come, come, lads," Grandfather was saying, but the great Mr. Derby only laughed.

"A little striving against each other does not hurt them," he said, "and a quick voyage brings profit to the Company. I will tell you this, young gentlemen. Down in the yards we are building a finer and larger ship than these two. The one who makes the best voyage out and back shall have the command of her when she is finished."

Even Grandfather's old eyes, with the tiny wind-marked wrinkles at the corners, lighted at the thought of such a prize. And Dan's face suddenly blazed with the fire of an idea.

"Uncle Tom," he said, taking the tall man by the sleeves of his coat, "Uncle Tom, let me go with you. My father would let me go, I know. Take me with you."

Young Captain Raeburn shook his head. "The crew is all made up, Dan, and there is no place for you. You might make us a good cabin boy, but I have one already."

Captain Samuel Horne flashed a smile at him. "I would take you myself, boy, if I had a place," he said.

Mr. Elias Derby had something to tell Grandfather and they went away down the stairs together, with the two young captains clattering after them. The children sat down beside old Jerry Green, the chief sailmaker, stitching away with his big sail needle with the shield across his palm instead of a thimble.

"I'm old enough to go, don't you think, Jerry?" Dan demanded.

Jerry nodded wisely. "Don't you be fretting, young sir. First and last, every likely boy that's born in Salem town goes away to sea."

Patty said nothing. Here was Dan talking of the voyages he was going to make, while girls had to stay at home. It was very hard. She sat quiet, looking out of the window at the ragged clouds racing past, holding the canvas smooth for Jerry, once in a while having to blink quickly to keep a tear back. Something soft and silent crept under her arm. The little cat, Tiger, had not gone home after all, and had stolen up the stairs to come rubbing against Patty's knee. She took the kitten into her lap. The soft purring was very comforting. She began to listen to Jerry's long story of his first voyage.

That evening, as they sat at supper, with the candle-light soft and bright on the silver that had come from England, and on the brass and copper bowls from the far Indies, Dan was telling Mother eagerly, "I tried to get Uncle Tom to take me with him and he said if he had a place he really would. What do you think, Mother?"

Pretty Mrs. Raeburn only sighed, but Grandfather declared, "It might have been a good chance. A year's voyaging, on a good ship, with a good captain, is a fine thing for any boy."

"I suppose so," Mother answered. "But there is no place for him, so we need not consider it." Patty knew from the sound of her voice how glad she was.

Very early in the morning Patty was wakened by Grandfather's voice at her door.

"The *Spitfire* and the *Adventure* are both getting up sail," he told her, "and they will be off with the turn of the tide. Call Dan, and come down to the point with me to see them pass."

It was a walk of three miles or more down to the point, with the dewy bayberry bushes sprinkling Patty's dress. The gray sky overhead was just lighting up at the edges with the clear yellow of morning. Once more Tiger came running after them and this time Patty picked her up.

When they got to the rocky point, they had to wait for nearly an hour, with a chill wind blowing over them. Patty wrapped herself and Tiger closely in her cloak, while Grandfather and Dan turned up the collars of their coats. None of the three dreamed of going back. Suddenly they turned about, listening. Running feet were coming along the path behind them, and soon old Robert, the house man, came stumbling over the last little rise.

"Mr. Dan, there was a message came, just after you left, from your uncle. Something happened to keep his cabin boy at home after all, and he wanted to take you. He said you must surely come." He was so breathless he could hardly speak and Dan fairly shook him by the arm.

"Did you send word where I was? Did he say he would wait for me?"

"The mistress thought you had just gone down to the wharf, so she threw some things into your father's old chest and had Tim take it down in the cart to be put on board. She sent me along to find you."

"Oh, quick, quick, we must get back," Dan cried.

But Patty pointed. "Look! It's too late. The ship has sailed."

She was right. The *Adventure* was leaning to the wind, coming down the harbor with the tide. Nothing would stop her now. The *Spitfire*, with spread sails, was coming after, tall, white, and stately, as the strong wind bore them both.

"Grandfather, Grandfather, what shall I do?" Dan asked.

"Come," was all that Grandfather answered. He hurried down the rough path to the little stretch of beach below. Not a hundred feet away was a fisherman's small house. A boat was drawn up on the shore, a tiny boat, but with stout oars and a little three-cornered sail.

"Of course! Jonathan Hull will lend his boat to us," Patty thought. Grandfather always knew what to do. He said, over his shoulder, to Robert, "Go home and tell your mistress that we will put the boy on board here at the mouth of the harbor."

"Say good-by to her for me," Dan shouted, joyous, excited. "Wait, Grandfather, I can launch her."

Jonathan Hull was not at home, so they all pushed together and got the little craft into the water. Under Grandfather's orders the two got up sail. The wind caught

them as they swung out from shore, and the boat tilted sharply. Tiger had clung to Patty's shoulder. Now she took the cat into her lap. There was water splashing in the bottom of the open dory and cats do not like wet feet.

They went through the long rollers and were soon out where the full wind caught them. When they would rise on a rolling crest, they saw the *Adventure* racing through the water, her long curly wake streaming out behind. Could they catch her? They had to catch her!

The boat danced like a cork. They could see the crew of the *Adventure* crowding to the rail to watch them. The wind carried the sound of orders, and dark figures began running up into the rigging. They swung the yards. The ship was slowing down.

283

"Drop the sail and take the oars," Grandfather ordered. A moment later the little boat was alongside the ship. A line was let down to them, and then a swinging rope ladder. Dan stood up, waited for the right chance, caught the ladder, and began to climb up. Patty sat watching, her face upturned.

Then suddenly she cried out, "Tiger, Tiger, come back." But the little cat had made a leap, and now was going up the ladder as neatly as though she were climbing the wisteria vines on the porch at home. She did not like the wet bobbing boat and seemed to think that the big ship above meant solid ground and safety. Dan caught her as she reached the rail and made as though he would drop her down again into the boat.

"No, no," Patty shouted, for there was every chance that the kitten would fall into the sea. The *Adventure* was gathering way again. The little boat was cast loose and swung free.

Dan was waving to them as the *Adventure* drew away. Behind her came the *Spitfire*, winged and swift. Her crew was waving, too, as the dory got up sail and made off toward shore. Neither Grandfather nor Patty said a word as they came to land.

THE HOME PORT

A hundred days and a hundred days and a hundred days make very nearly a year, but not quite. Grandfather told Patty often enough, in the months that passed, that the voyage might be much longer. But Patty counted the time very carefully and knew just when she was going to expect them home, the *Adventure*, Uncle Tom, Dan, and Tiger. She thought about them all when she woke in the morning, while she was in school, when she said her prayers at night. Time moved very slowly through the spring, through the summer, through the beginning of autumn.

A ship came in from India bringing news of the two vessels. They had reached Calcutta within two days of each other. The *Spitfire* had come in first, but each had made a wonderful run — eighty-nine days and ninety-one days. Very few ships had ever made the voyage in so little time.

Mr. Derby's agent had cargoes waiting, so that they could load quickly and be soon on the homeward voyage. It was said that they were to start the middle of September, and that it was arranged that the *Spitfire* should sail two days ahead of the *Adventure*, since that was the advantage she had won.

Patty counted the days again. They should be back on the tenth of December. And she was sure that the *Adventure* would come to port first.

"At this time of year the bad weather may delay them," Grandfather warned her. He was happy that his son had done so well. People said of Tom Raeburn that he was sometimes overcautious, that he would not put on all sail in a stiff wind, that he loved his ship too much to risk her safety. He must be learning when to be careful and when to be bold, for this was a splendid record, even though the *Spitfire* had done better.

December was beginning, clear and cold, then stormy. Every day Patty went up to the cupola at the top of the house, from which one could look all the way down the harbor. Usually, Grandfather went with her.

"We shall have to be patient," Grandfather told her again and again. On that special afternoon of the third of December he was saying it once more. "You must have patience. It may be a month yet."

But in that very second Patty had seen something that made her catch her breath. Tall white sails were showing beyond the point, two masts, three. Anyone living in Salem knew the outline of every ship as he knew the face of every friend. Was it the *Spitfire?* No! It was the *Adventure*.

She came up the harbor as swiftly and surely as though all the will and all the hope of those on shore were drawing her home. She swung about proudly and dropped her anchor with a splash. The Raeburns were all on the wharf, waiting for the first boat to come across the water with its swiftly moving oars. There was Dan. Even as he sat in the boat Patty could see how he had grown, how brown his face was, what a mop of wind-blown hair he had. He came ashore with a duffel bag over his shoulder and a flat Indian basket under his arm. How his face lit when he saw them!

Somebody in the crowd behind Patty was saying, "Mr. Derby is from home. 'Tis a pity he did not see his ship

come in." Uncle Tom Raeburn was still on board, attending to last matters.

Soon Dan was at home, by his own fireside. He had just put down his bag and the basket in the corner, when Mr. Elias Derby came hurrying in.

"I could not wait," he said. "I knew Captain Raeburn was still on board, so I thought I could get the best account from the boy here. Tell me, Dan, what of the *Spitfire?*"

"You won't see her for a few days still, sir," Dan told him. "We sailed two days after her from Calcutta, and we sighted her off the island of Madeira, but after that we left her behind."

Mr. Derby looked thoughtful. "There has been some bad weather over the Atlantic in these last weeks. I had always thought your uncle was a cautious man in a heavy wind. Has he changed his ways so much?"

Dan was silent for a moment, then he spoke bravely. "He would want me to tell you the truth," he answered. "It happened that a piece of good luck came to us. We were chased by a pirate. A great black ship flying the black flag came up and took after us, instead of after the *Spitfire.* We had to make a run for it, I can tell you. For two days she hung at our heels. It was blowing great guns, and Uncle Tom cracked on all the sail he had. He said he would rather lose the *Adventure* to Davy Jones than to the pirates. We managed to get away — and we had left the *Spitfire* a long way behind."

Mr. Derby was delighted with the tale. He shook hands with Dan and went away. Some day Dan would command a ship for him too, so he said, and Dan's face glowed and so did Grandfather's.

The moment Mr. Derby was out of the house, Patty asked the question which she could not keep back, "Dan, what about Tiger?"

Dan opened the basket. Out came Tiger, grown to a big, smooth, splendid cat now, a cat who knew the world and her own place in it. And after her came another, a marvelous cat, cloudy gray, with a thick soft coat and a tail like a plume. The newcomer made a jump to Dan's shoulder, but Tiger made straight for her mistress's lap.

"Tiger was the pet of the ship," Dan told her. "She was wonderful at catching rats. I thought the crew of the *Adventure* would never give her back to you, so we bought this Persian cat in Calcutta to bring home. He was lazy at first and did not want to do his work on board. Then he got a little hungry and Tiger showed him a thing or two. Now he is as good a ship's cat as you could ask. You are to choose, Patty, either Tiger or the Persian, and we will keep the other."

Patty did not need any time to choose. Tiger was her cat. Tiger was purring on her knee, her eyes closed down to narrow slits. She was dreaming of far, strange sights that Patty had never seen, but her deep purring sound showed how contented she was. Even ship's cats like to come home.

Cornelia Meigs

A DONKEY IN THE NEW WORLD

HE was a Spanish donkey in the beginning, for he was born in the province of Granada. It was to be expected that he would spend his life making his sure-footed way up and down the steep paths of its mountains, carrying heavy loads in the panniers hung across his back.

But one day strange things began to happen to him. He was led down a path where he had never been before, to the edge of water that was far wider than the little stream which ran through his native valley. Other donkeys were there by the water, and many tall horses, too. One by one they were all led, or pushed and pulled if they held back, along a narrow wooden board and into a house that rested on the water and that tipped and rocked as they were driven into it.

Then began a hard time. The little donkey had always prided himself on being able to keep upright, and not slip, even on the steepest paths. That was why his master called him a good little donkey. But now there were times when the floor under him tipped, so that he could not hold his footing but slid from side to side and sometimes fell on the other animals. They all learned that it was just as well not to try to scramble up, when these bad times came. They lay still as they had fallen, until the floor was level again.

The men who fed and looked after them were good to them. But the animals all grew very tired of being cooped up in the hot, dark place, for they had always lived out-of-doors, where there was plenty of air and sunshine. One day there were many noises over their heads, and the boat stopped moving and stood still. They pricked up their ears and listened, hoping that they were going to get out. But the moving began again, and they were still in the hot, dark place.

Then came the worst time of all. The little donkey thought that he had become used to a floor that rocked back and forth. But the tipping grew worse and worse, and there were loud sounds of things falling, and the shouts of men as if they were afraid. All at once there was a great crash, and the floor stood straight up and down. Then the roof over their heads was gone, and suddenly water came flooding in.

The little donkey kicked and fought as the water swept over him. The next thing he knew he was in the flood, paddling with his legs. There was fresh air, and he was alone, with no other donkeys or horses in sight. He had not known that he could swim, but as he kicked with his feet, he stayed up in the water. Still, he grew very tired of keeping his legs moving. After a long, long time, his feet touched something solid. He pushed on it, and walked up out of the water onto a sandy beach. There he fell and lay still, drawing long, panting breaths.

He did not know it, but he had found South America, all by himself. The ship on which he had crossed the ocean had been wrecked in the Caribbean Sea, near the coast of what is now called Colombia, and he was the only living thing from that ship to come ashore on South American soil.

That day some Indians who lived far back in the mountains had come down to the seashore on an expedition. All of a sudden they heard a strange, loud sound such as they had never heard in all their lives before. It was the little donkey braying. He was lonely, and he was hungry. So he had gotten up on his feet and begun to bray loudly. That was a sound which was new to South America.

The Indians came timidly through the heavy vegetation, which reached almost to the water's edge, and peered through the leafy branches to see what was making this terrifying sound. There stood this queer animal, the like of which they had never seen before, holding his head high and opening his mouth to make the shrill, high noise. In Spain, where there were horses, the donkey had seemed small. But these Indians had never seen a horse, and to them he seemed very big. They could see that he was wet, and knew that he must have walked out of the sea.

For a while they stood and watched him, talking excitedly among themselves. He, hearing their voices, pricked up his ears and walked toward them. They all ran back in fright, and he stood still and looked at them. One man, who was bolder than the rest, walked forward. The donkey put out his nose in friendly fashion, and the Indian touched him and stroked his wet coat. Then they all came out from their hiding-place in the jungle and stared at him. But they stood a little way off, waiting to see if a good or an evil spirit lived in him. It was plain to them that he was not an ordinary animal, but something supernatural, like a god, that had come up out of the sea.

They tried to lead him away with them, for they must return to their high mountain home. Ordinarily the little donkey would have been more than ready to climb, but now he was exhausted by his long swim and the lack of food. They managed to sling him on a tree-trunk which they cut, with his feet held off the ground, as they would have carried one of their smaller creatures. He was heavy, and they had to take turns as they carried him up the crooked, rocky mountain path. But at last they hauled him up to their village of Tairona, where they were received with great excitement. Surely the village to which such a visitor had come would be lucky. They must give him a comfortable home and treat him with honor and respect.

So the little donkey lived a peaceful life for several months as the honored guest of the Indians.

CONQUEST

Far down on the seacoast, west of the beach where the little donkey had come ashore, there was a Spanish settlement of Santa Marta, founded ten years earlier by the first white man to land on this shore. The leader had died, and a large, new expedition had come out from Spain in this year 1535, to take possession of the country and explore the region back of the coast.

The expedition was a strange one to have come to these lonely shores. The governor for the new colony arrived with all pomp and dignity, accompanied by cavaliers in silks, with velvet cloaks and polished armor. With them came ladies, too, who expected to find comfortable houses in which to dwell. Instead, they found a miserable little village on a bare beach, with the earlier colonists living in rude huts, buying such food as could be obtained from the Indians.

The sailors who had brought the expedition overseas demanded their pay, and the cavaliers and ladies pressed the governor to produce the gold which was said to be abundant in these parts. If the men did not get it, they would sail back to Spain.

The governor was in a difficult position. He sent parties of soldiers into the country with orders to capture Indian towns and seize such gold as they might find there. One such company heard that the two most powerful chiefs of the Indians, by name Marobare and Arobare, had found refuge from the pursuing Spaniards in the town of Tairona, far up in the mountains. Probably there would be gold there. They must go and see.

The path upward was so steep that no man could walk it alone. They held each other in a living chain to avoid falling over the precipices and into the gorges below. Yet they pushed on, hoping to surprise the Indians in the village, which must be at the end of this path. All at once the weary climbers heard a sound which carried them back across the ocean to the homeland they had left. They heard a donkey bray.

"It can't be," one said.

"There isn't a donkey anywhere in this forsaken land,

except the ones we brought with us to Santa Marta," another declared.

"We're just hearing things!" remarked a third.

Across the air sounded again the bray of a donkey.

"Some Indian has heard a donkey down in the village on the shore, and is imitating the sound, to draw us away by a path where they will attack us," said another soldier.

But they could not stop to make any more guesses, for there was the Indian village before them, and they must attack it before the inhabitants came out against them. They did this, and overpowered the people, and took a large amount of gold in images and ornaments which they found in the houses. Then they came upon the little donkey, who had been living in such comfort with the Indians for all these months.

The Indians told the Spaniards how he had come ashore, and how they had managed to carry him up the steep path. The soldiers promptly ordered them to carry him down again in the same way, which they were very reluctant to do. But the Spaniards were not going to leave a good little donkey from the homeland up there in an Indian village.

Down in Santa Marta, the donkey, whom the soldiers named Marobare after the chieftain of the captured village, found himself with other donkeys and horses that had followed him across the sea. No longer was he a guest, held almost in worship by those with whom he dwelt. He was put to work, to carry heavy loads on his back and clamber up and down the steep paths. But Marobare was a good little donkey, and did not mind work.

Indeed, he was the only donkey chosen to go on the famous expedition which went inland shortly, led by Don Gonzalo Quesada, a lawyer-explorer from Spain, who was to conquer the great Chibcha Indian nation. At least he is the only donkey of whom the chroniclers tell.

No one would have recognized Marobare on that trip up the Magdalena River. He hardly knew himself, for he was covered, like all the big horses, with a headpiece and a blanket that looked exactly like a white, tufted quilt. This was to protect the animals from the poisoned arrows of the Indians. The big company of eight hundred men and one hundred horses — and one donkey! — were traveling

through a region of thick forest and jungle, cutting their way as they went. Hostile Indians, who wished to keep them out of the country, shot at them from behind high rocks and out of thickets. The men had found that regular armor did not do much good, for the arrows pierced through it. But they did not go through this cotton armor, worn by both man and beast, which had layers of cotton, "three fingers thick," quilted between folds of linen and sewed with rough thread. Each horse had one piece to guard his face and chest, and another which hung down over his back and legs.

The soldiers cared as much to protect their horses as themselves, for horses were extremely valuable to the would-be conquerors of South America. There were those who said that a horse was worth five times as much as a man on such an expedition as this against the Indians. Besides their usefulness in carrying their masters on their backs, they were valuable because of the fear they inspired in the natives, who thought that men riding on such beasts must be more than human.

Some horses and a far greater number of men died on that terrible journey of many months. But Marobare survived, and came out with his companions on that high point which looked over the beautiful, fertile plain of Bogotá.

When the leaders came out on the spot where they could look down on the beautiful, well-watered plain, with its native villages, they stood still and cried out with pleasure, "Oh, goodly land! Land that ends our woes!"

But Marobare and the horses that had reached there first did not look up. They were too busy cropping the grass at their feet.

From this time on, the donkey seems to have served chiefly one of the two priests, or friars, whom Quesada had brought along. Probably he carried on his back the little altar which the friar set up when he wished to conduct a service of worship for the Indians. Perhaps he brought that altar to the place where, one fine day, Quesada took possession of the country in the name of the King of Spain, and marked the circle where the first twelve houses of the new city of Bogotá should be placed.

Later Marobare brought comfort to two soldiers by his cheerful braying. They had been sent as messengers on a raiding trip against the Indians, and had been caught outside a town at nightfall. Seeing no lights and hearing no sounds, they were fearful lest the army had moved on and left them to become the prey of wandering warriors. They waited all night in some thick bushes where they could hide themselves, and then, as daylight came, they heard in the town the braying of a donkey.

"Marobare! Marobare!" they cried joyfully, and hastened to the camp from which the sound came.

Today, descendants of Marobare, donkeys by hundreds and thousands, climb the steep mountain trails of Colombia and Venezuela with heavy burdens on their backs. None do it more cheerfully than did Marobare, the "valiant quadruped," as the Spaniards called him.

Marion F. Lansing

TRAMP, THE SHEEP DOG

Boys! Some varmint around here has been killing our sheep. I believe it's that yellow pup there! And the very first time any of you catch him acting suspicious, let him have it. Shoot him on the spot! Do you hear?"

Tramp never moved. He just lay there, stretched out, his head resting on his paws. It was only a short time since he had wandered into Clem Tyler's place, from no one knew where, a scrawny, hungry, half-grown little cur of a pup. Immediately, he had made himself at home.

There was no place on the ranch for a stray dog and he never would have been allowed to hang around if it hadn't been for old Ruff. Ruff was the greatest sheep dog in those parts and his word was law. So, when he made friends with the stranger, shared his food with him, and looked out for him, that settled it.

After a while, Ruff commenced to teach him the sheep-tending business. But Tramp didn't seem to pay any attention. He wanted to play. He wanted action. He saw no fun in lying around all day long with a bunch of sheep as Ruff did, pretending he was minding them. He wanted to chase sheep and see them run. He wanted to bark and yap at them. And that was one thing Ruff wouldn't stand for. Ruff would sail in and give Tramp a good licking.

But one day, poor old Ruff died of old age. After that, Clem had to look out for his sheep himself. He allowed Tramp to go along but he never let the dog stay with the sheep during the day. Clem didn't trust that stray dog from nowhere.

As winter approached, sheep began to disappear. No trace of the killer could be found, but just because there wasn't anyone else to blame, the finger of suspicion was pointed straight at Tramp. Even his master accused him, and had given an order to the men to watch him and shoot him down on the slightest excuse. A sheep-killer is a despised thing, but the men did not like the idea of shooting a dog in cold blood.

One afternoon, storm clouds began to bank up in the west. Clem knew they were in for a bad snow-storm. The wind was rising, and it was bitterly cold. Clem decided to get the sheep in early. He called Tramp, but Tramp was not around. And no wonder — it wasn't sheep time for him. So Clem hustled down to the pasture without the dog.

When he came up the road with the sheep, there stood

Tramp, his head hanging in shame, his tail curled between his legs, as if he expected to be scolded for not being on the job. Clem paid no attention to him. The dog just stood there and watched as his master drove the flock through the yard. He never took his eyes off the sheep as they filed through the gate. He noticed that one was missing. He could tell. He had learned how to count sheep from Ruff even if nobody knew it. They couldn't fool him! Not Tramp! Now that Ruff was gone, Tramp felt responsible for those sheep. That was his job now even if Clem didn't trust him.

That night the storm broke. It was a raging blizzard. Tramp watched it from the back porch. He was so uneasy he couldn't eat his dinner of corn bread and cracklings. He couldn't sleep. He would get up and then lie down again. Meanwhile, the storm grew worse and worse.

Finally, Tramp got up, took a good stretch, and slipped out into the bitter cold and the driving snow. He headed down the road, toward the pasture. He hunted and searched the pasture, backward and forward, while the snow coated him white. At last, way over on the far side of the pasture, right at the edge of the woods, he found what he had been looking for — the missing sheep. Beside her was a wobbly little black-faced lamb not more than a few hours old.

The mother was bleating pitifully, making a terrible fuss. The little lamb could hardly stand up, it was so weak. But Tramp did not hesitate. He went into action. He tried to drive them, but they wouldn't drive. He barked at

them, snapping at the mother's hind legs, but she wouldn't budge. She just turned round and round in silly sheep fashion. Then Tramp tackled the lamb. But no sooner did he touch it than down in the snow it would go. Then it would have a hard time struggling to its feet. Finally it sank down, lay still, and couldn't get up again. It was too far gone to struggle.

That decided Tramp. He left the lamb where it was and commenced again on the mother. He snarled and snapped at her, and he even bit her. He behaved exactly as he had seen Ruff behave. Finally, he got her started. He drove her out of the woods, into the field, then across it and onto the road. He headed her up toward the house.

Never letting up for a single second, he drove the terrified sheep through the raging storm. Time and time again she would stop in her silly way, and try to scoot off in another direction. But Tramp would fly at her, head her off, and set her going up the road again. At last they came to the barnyard but it was closed up tight for the night. So Tramp drove her into the wagon shed and made her stay there.

The dog's barking and the sheep's bleating started a big commotion. Every creature on the place woke up. The chickens, the pigs, the cows, and the horses — all of them commenced to fret. The fuss even woke Clem, who figured that something was after his sheep. He jumped up and raised the window as a shadow flitted across the yard. He shot off both barrels of his shotgun at once. There was a yelp, a cry of pain.

That convinced Clem that at last he had caught the sheep-killer, right in the act! And, just as he had suspected, the criminal was Tramp. He recognized that yelp. Clem went back to bed and slept through the night.

The next morning, the storm had lessened. The ground was covered deep with snow. Clem went out to take care of the stock, and the first thing he ran across was the mother sheep in the wagon shed, just standing there. That puzzled him. How had she come there? Then he began looking for the dog he had killed. But he couldn't find a trace of it, not a trace! The snow had hidden all evidence.

Just then, through the storm, he heard a faint howl far away. Quickly Clem got his gun and two other men, and they started searching for the wounded dog.

They plowed their way through the drifts, stopping

now and then to listen to the howl. It came and went but
they could make their way by it. Down the lane they
went, to the pasture. Across the pasture the howling led
them to the woods. And there — the sight they saw
startled them. There lay poor Tramp, looking up at them.
His tail was wagging very feebly. His back was all
matted with blood where the shot had peppered it. Snow
was banked up on all sides around him. Alongside him,
snuggled up close, cozy and warm, was a little, black-
faced baby lamb. It was alive and kicking and just as
frisky as could be.

Then they knew that Tramp wasn't a sheep-killer. He
was a loyal sheep dog, just as old Ruff had been. One of
them picked up the lamb and stuck it under his coat, while
Clem tried to show Tramp his suspicions were gone.
Down on his knees in the snow he went and drew Tramp
to him and hugged him.

"Just what I've been looking for!" Clem said, his eyes
misty, as he stroked the homely head. "A good sheep
dog! The only trouble was I didn't have sense enough to
look in the right place!"

Don Lang

IN South America there is a river called the Yabebiri, which flows through the territory of Misiones. In this river there are many rays, which give the stream its name, for "Yabebiri" means "river of ray fish."

The ray is a kind of mud fish like the salt water skate. It is a wide, flat fish with a long, slender tail. The tail is very bony. When it strikes, it cuts, leaving poison in the wound. The pain from a ray bite is one of the sharpest pains one can feel.

There are also other kinds of fish in the Yabebiri, most of them good to eat. That is why some evil men began to fish in the river with dynamite. The shock of the explosion stunned and killed all the fish near by — not only the big ones, but also the little ones, which are too small to be eaten.

Now there was a man who lived on the bank of the river who thought that it was very cruel and wasteful to hunt fish with dynamite. He was sorry for the fish, especially the little ones. He told the men who were doing so that they must stop. At first they were angry and said that they would do as they pleased. But the man was known everywhere to be an upright, honest man, and finally they obeyed him and set off no more bombs in the river.

The fish were grateful to this man, whom they had

come to know the moment he approached the edge of the water. Whenever he walked along the bank, the rays, especially, would swim along the bottom to keep him company. He, of course, did not know he had so many friends in the river. He lived there simply because he liked the place.

Now it happened one afternoon that a fox came running down to the river. Putting his forepaws into the water, he called to the rays, "Quick! Quick! Here comes that friend of yours. He's in trouble!"

All the rays who heard him came swimming up anxiously to the edge of the water.

"What's the matter? Where is he?" they asked.

"Here he comes," answered the fox. "He has been fighting with a panther, and is trying to get away. He wants to get over to that island. Let him cross, for he is a very good man."

"Of course we will! Of course we will!" the rays answered. "As for the panther, we will attend to him."

"Yes, but remember that a panther is a panther," said the fox. He meant that a panther is almost as hard to fight as a tiger. The fox gave a little jump and ran back into the woods, so as not to be near when the panther came.

A minute or two later the branches along the river bank were pushed aside, and the man came running down to the water's edge. He was bleeding and his shirt was torn. It was clear that the man was very badly hurt, for he almost fell as he ran out into the river. When he put his feet into the water, the rays moved aside so that their tails would not touch him. He waded across to the island, with the water coming up to his breast. On the other side he fell to the ground fainting from loss of blood.

The rays did not have much time to sit there pitying him. Some distance behind the man the panther came leaping. The big wildcat stopped on the bank and gave a great roar of rage. Up and down the river the rays called, "The panther! The panther!" as they gathered along the shore to attack him if he tried to cross.

The panther looked up and down the stream for the man, and finally spied him lying helpless on the island. With another howl, the beast leaped into the water. Almost instantly, however, he felt as though a hundred pins and needles were sticking into his paws. The rays were trying to block the ford, and were stinging him with the stingers in their tails. He gave one big jump back to the river bank and stood there roaring and holding one paw up in the air because it hurt him to step on it. After a moment he looked down into the water and saw that it was all muddy. The rays were coming in great crowds, stirring up the bottom of the river as they came.

"Aha!" said the panther. "Aha! I see! It was you, you wicked ray fish, it was you who gave me all those stings. Well, now, just get out of the way."

"We will not get out of the way," answered the rays.

"Away, I tell you!" said the panther.

"We won't!" said the rays. "This man has been good to us, and as long as he lives on the river we intend to protect him."

308

"Get out of my way!" roared the panther furiously.

"Never!" said the rays.

"Well, we'll see!" said the panther, with another great roar.

He ran up the bank to get a start for one great leap. The panther saw that the rays were packed close in along the shore. He figured that if he could jump far out into the stream, he would be beyond them and their stingers, and thus could finally reach the wounded man on the island.

But some of the rays saw what he was intending to do, and they began to shout to one another, "Out to midstream! He's going to jump!"

The panther did succeed in making a very long leap,

and for some seconds after he struck the water he felt no pain. He gave a great roar of delight, thinking he had deceived his enemies. But then, all of a sudden, he felt a sting here and a sting there, in front, in back, on his sides. The rays had turned upon him again, driving their poisonous stingers into his skin.

For a moment the panther thought it was as easy to go forward as back, and so he kept on. But as the rays were now ranged along the shore of the island, the panther turned and went back to the shore he had left. He had to lie down on his side to keep his wounded feet off the ground, and he was breathing deeply from pain and fatigue.

The rays were not satisfied, however. They kept crowding up along the shore because they knew that a panther never travels alone, but always with a mate. Sure enough, the she-panther soon came roaring through the bushes to rescue her husband. She looked across to the island where the man was lying wounded, and then at her mate, who lay there panting at her feet. Then she looked down into the water, which was black with rays.

"Ray fish!" she called.

"Well, madam?" answered the rays.

"Let me cross the river."

"No crossing here for panthers," said the rays.

"I'll bite your tails off," said the she-panther.

"Even without our tails, we won't let you cross," said the rays.

"For the last time, out of my way!" said the she-panther.

The she-panther now put one foot into the water. A ray struck at her and stung her right between two of her toes.

"Ouch!" growled the she-panther.

She sucked her paw and scowled. Then she turned and trotted off up the bank into the woods without saying another word.

But the rays understood what she was up to. She was going to some place farther along the stream where there were no rays and would swim across before they could reach her.

"Oh, oh!" they cried to one another. "Now our poor man-friend is done for. How can we let the rays down there know that we must prevent the panther from crossing at any cost?"

A little ray, who was a very bright and clever little fish, spoke up and said, "Get the shiners to carry a message. Shiners can swim like lightning, and they too ought to be grateful to the man for stopping those bombs."

"That's it! That's it! Let's send the shiners!"

A school of shiners happened to be going by, and so the rays sent them off with a message to all the rays along the river: "Sting the she-panther if she tries to cross! Hold the ford against the she-panther!"

Though the shiners swam very, very fast, they were barely in time. The panther was already in the water, and had begun to swim out beyond her depth. In fact, she was almost over on the other side toward the island. But when her paws struck bottom and she began to wade again, the rays were on hand. They rushed in packs upon her legs and feet, stinging them with tens, hundreds, thousands of stings. At the same time more rays crowded in between the panther and the shore. Roaring with pain and anger, she finally swam back to the place where she had jumped in, and rolled about on the ground in agony. When she came back to where her husband was lying, her paws and legs were all swollen from the poison.

To the Rescue

The rays, for their part, were getting very tired from all this stinging and hurrying to and fro. And they were not much relieved when they saw the panther and the she-panther get up all of a sudden and go off into the woods. The rays were very much worried, and they gathered together in council.

"Do you know what I think?" said the oldest ray. "I think they have gone off to get all the other panthers. When they come back, they will be too much for us and they will surely get across!"

"That is so!" said the other rays, the older and more experienced ones. "At least one or two will get across. That will be the end of our friend, the man! Suppose we go and have a talk with him!"

For the first time they now went over to the place where the man was lying. They had been too busy up to that time to think of him.

The man had lost a great deal of blood, and was still

lying on the ground, but he was able to sit up enough to talk. The rays told him how they had been defending the ford against the panthers who had been trying to eat him. The man could hardly keep from weeping as he thought of the friendship of these fishes. He thanked them by reaching out his hand and stroking the nearest ones on the nose. But then he moaned, "Alas! You cannot save me. When the panthers come back, there will be many of them. If they want to get across they can."

"No, they can't," said a little ray. "No, they can't. Nobody but a friend of ours can cross this ford!"

"I'm afraid they will be too much for you," said the man sadly. After a moment's thought he added, "There might be one way to stop them. If there were someone to go and get my rifle — I have a Winchester, with a box of bullets — but the only friends I have near here are fish — and fish can't bring me a rifle."

"Well — ?" asked the rays anxiously.

"Yes, yes," said the man, rubbing his forehead with his right hand, as though trying to collect his thoughts. "Let's see. Once I had a friend, a river hog whom I tamed and kept in my house to play with my children. One day he got homesick and went back to the woods to live. I don't know what became of him, but I think he came to this neighborhood!"

The rays gave one great shout of joy.

"We know him! We know him! He lives in the cave just below here in the river bank. We remember now that he once told us he knew you very well. We will send him to get the rifle."

No sooner said than done! A shiner, who was the fastest swimmer in his school, started off down the river to the place where the river hog lived. It was not far away, and before long the river hog came up on the bank across the river. The man picked up a fishbone from the ground near him. Dipping it in some blood that was on his hand, he wrote on a dry leaf this letter to his wife:

DEAR WIFE:

Send me my Winchester by this river hog, with a full box of a hundred bullets.

(Signed) THE MAN

He was just finishing the letter when the whole river valley began to tremble with the most frightful roars. The panthers were coming back in a large company to force a crossing and devour their enemy. Quickly two rays stuck their heads out of the water. The man handed them the leaf with the letter written on it, and holding it up clear of the water, they swam over to where the river hog was. He took it in his mouth and ran off as fast as he could toward the man's house.

There was no time to lose. The roaring was now very close to the river and every moment it was getting nearer. The rays called anxiously to the shiners, who were hovering in the water near by, waiting for orders, "Quick, shiners! Swim up and down the river, and give a general alarm! Have all the rays gather about the island on every side! We'll see whether these panthers can get across!"

A Terrible Battle

The panthers appeared at last. With a great roar an army of them came leaping down to the river bank. There were a hundred of them, at least. But, on the other hand, the river was now packed with rays who were ready to die rather than let a single panther cross.

"Get out of our way!" roared the panthers.

"No crossing this river!" said the rays.

"If you don't get out of the way, we will eat every ray, and every son of a ray, and every grandson of a ray, not counting the women and children," said the panthers.

"Perhaps," said the rays. "But no panther, nor any son, grandson, daughter, granddaughter, sister, brother, wife, aunt, or uncle of a panther will ever get across this ford."

"For one last time, get out of the way!"

"Never!" "Never!" "Never!" said the rays, one and all, with great determination.

Then the battle began. With enormous bounds and leaps, the panthers plunged into the river. They landed on an almost solid floor of ray fish. The rays plunged their stingers into the panthers' feet, and at each prick the panthers would send up the most blood-curdling roars. Meanwhile hundreds of rays were caught and torn by the panthers' claws, and went floating down the Yabebiri, which was soon all stained with ray blood. Still, they held their ground, though many more of the rays were being trampled on and scratched and bitten. But the panthers were getting terribly stung, too, and many of them had to go back to the shore, where they lay roaring and whining, holding their swollen paws up in the air.

After half an hour, the panthers were tired out and went back to the shore they came from, where they sat down to rest and to lick the stings on their paws.

"We cannot stand a second attack like this one," said the rays. "Hey, shiners! Go up and down the river again, and bring us reinforcements. We must have every single ray there is in the Yabebiri."

Again the shiners were off up and down the river, flecking the surface of the water with the wakes they left. The rays now thought they should consult the man again.

"We cannot hold out much longer," said the rays. And some of them actually wept for the poor man who was going to be eaten by the panthers.

"Never mind, please, my dear little rays," answered

the man. "You have done enough for me. It's a pity that any more of you should die. Now you had better let the panthers come across."

"Never!" cried the rays. "So long as there is a ray left alive, we shall defend the man who defended us."

"My dear friends," said the man in reply, "I think I am bound to die anyway, I am so badly wounded. But I can promise you that when that Winchester arrives, you will see some exciting things. That much I am sure of!"

"Yes, we know! We know!" said the rays. But they could not continue the conversation. The battle was on again. The panthers had now rested, and were crouching on the river bank, ready to take off with great leaps and bounds.

"We'll give you one last chance," they called to the rays. "Now be reasonable! Get out of our way!"

"Never!" said the rays, crowding up close along the shore in front of the panthers.

In a flash the panthers were in the water again, and the same terrible fight as before was taking place. The Yabebiri from shore to shore was one mass of bloody foam. Hundreds and hundreds of rays were tossed into the air, while the panthers bellowed from the pain in their paws.

The panthers, however, were little by little forcing their way forward. In vain the shiners darted up and down the river calling in more and more rays to battle. There were no rays left anywhere along the stream. Every one was either fighting desperately in the army around

317

the island, or was floating bruised and bleeding and helpless down the current.

At last they realized that the battle was lost. Five of
the biggest panthers had broken through the lines of the
rays, and were swimming through the clear water straight
toward the island. The poor rays decided they would
rather die than see their poor friend eaten by the panthers.

"Retreat to the island!" they called to one another.
"Back to the island!"

But alas, this was too late! Two more panthers had
now broken through the line. When the rays started for
the island, every panther on the shore jumped into the
water and made for the wounded man. Ten, twenty, fifty,
perhaps a hundred panthers could be seen swimming with
only their heads out of water.

But what was down below there? The rays had been
so busy fighting they had not noticed before. From a
point on the shore some distance below the ford, a brown,
fuzzy animal had gone into the water, and had been swim-

318

ming all this time toward the island. It was the river hog,
paddling along as fast as he could, with his head and neck
out of the water and the Winchester rifle in his mouth.
He was holding his head up to keep the rifle dry. On the
end of the rifle hung the man's cartridge belt, full of bullets.

The man gave a great cry of joy, for the river hog was
some distance ahead of the panthers and would get to him
in time. The man was too weak to move much, and so
the river hog pulled him around by the collar so that he
lay facing the panthers. In this position the man loaded
the rifle and took aim.

C-r-r-ack! C-r-r-r-ack! Bing! Bing! The rays who
had given up hope for their friend suddenly saw a panther,
who was just coming up out of the river toward the man,
give a great leap into the air and fall back to the ground.

The rays understood. "Hoo-ray! Hoo-ray! Hoo-ray!"
they shouted. "The man has the rifle! He is saved!"
And they started to dance on the bottom of the river.

C-r-r-r-ack! C-r-r-ack! Bing-g-g! Bing-g-g! The rifle

319

kept going off and the bullets kept singing through the air. At each shot a panther fell dead on the sand or sank drowning under the water. The shooting did not last more than a minute and a half, however. After ten or a dozen panthers had been killed, the others swam back to the opposite shore and ran off into the woods.

The panthers that were killed in the water sank to the bottom, where the horned pouts ate them. Others kept afloat, and the shiners went down the Yabebiri with them, all the way to the Parana, having a great feast off panther meat, and jumping and hopping along the top of the water to express their delight. When the friends of the wounded man came to get him, they skinned the panthers that were lying on the shore, and the man's wife had a set of new rugs for her dining room.

Soon the man got well again. And the rays, who have a great many children each year, were as numerous as ever after one season. The man was so grateful for what they had done in trying to save his life that he built a bungalow on the island, and went there to live during his vacations. On nights in summer when the moon was shining, he would go out in front of his bungalow and sit down on a rock overlooking the water. The rays would creep up softly over the bottom and point him out to fish who did not know him.

"There he is, see? The panthers came across over here; we stood in line over there. And when the panthers broke through, the man took his rifle, and . . . ."

Horacio Quiroga

HOCUS-POCUS

P. T. BARNUM

COME see the two-horned jigamaree
And the gen-uine mermaid rare!
The elephants in their Sunday pants
And the dangerous polar bear!
This way, this way, for the freaks at play
And the cold pink lemonade!
For Barnum's fooling the world again!
Barnum's on parade!

Oh, tootle the rope of the callyope!
Whang on the big bass drum!
Let the welkin ring for the Showman King
And General Tom Thumb!
For Jenny Lind of the musical wind
And Jumbo, London's pride,
And all of the Greatest Show On Earth
Ere P. T. Barnum died!

For freaks were the joy of this Bethel boy,
And he knew folks paid to see 'em,
And anything new they'd troop to view
In his marvelous Dime Museum.
By hook or crook, he would make them look
If he had to bloom like a crocus.
Oh, the marvelous lies that Barnum told!
The wonderful hocus-pocus!

Walk in, walk in, let the show begin!
Don't let those children wait!
The lions snort and the clowns cavort
And Barnum stands by the gate.
His Yankee eyes are merry with lies,
He's telling a gilded story.
Oh, the marvelous show that Barnum gave
In his humbug days of glory!

Rosemary and *Stephen Vincent Benét*

PHINEAS," remarked his father, pushing back his coffee cup and carefully wiping the ends of his walrus mustache, "you can tend store for me the next two or three days. The mare's going to take your mother and me to the county seat." He looked across the table at his thirteen-year-old son with decision and with more satisfaction than he intended to express to the boy.

Phineas Taylor Barnum, a sturdy, broad-shouldered lad, stopped munching a doughnut and his eyes danced. This piece of news was too good to be true. He had often helped his father in the store but to have it in charge — that would be wonderful!

"Yes, sir," he answered, respectfully.

His father went briskly on with his instructions. "Don't give the Widow Sweeney any credit. Cash in hand is the rule, unless circumstances is a mite unusual. Seeing apples is good this year, you can take two or three barrels in exchange for groceries. But, remember, business is likely to be brisk and you're to tend to your job and not talk your head off. You've got a good head on your shoulders when you choose to use it. That's all. And don't make me use that strap hanging up in the barn when I come back Saturday." The keen eyes twinkled slightly.

Having delivered this warning, Barnum Senior, citizen of the town of Bethel, Connecticut, went to hitch up.

Barnum Junior, rejoicing in his unexpected job, put on his hat, and took his way to his father's corner store.

Since a chill October wind was blowing, he began his business day with what his father would have called a needless extravagance. He started a fire in the rusty iron stove in the center of the store. The fire, made out of shavings, old boxes, and sawdust, had not been going fifteen minutes before Phineas's first customer arrived. It was the Widow Sweeney, shawled and bonneted, peering out of her near-sighted eyes. She slammed the store door so that everything on the shelves rattled. Delighted by the good fire, she crept near it, untying her bonnet strings.

"Well, so it's Barnum's boy!" she remarked in a pleased tone. The son should be much easier to deal with than the father.

"Now I want you," she continued, consulting a list, "to tie up a pound of white sugar and two pounds of coffee and a pound of rice and a pint of sorghum molasses."

Young Barnum went to the shelves and began weighing out the various articles, to which the Widow Sweeney kept adding other items. At last everything was ready. In his pleasantest tone, he stated, "One dollar, if you please, Mrs. Sweeney."

The Widow started back. "No sass from you, Phineas Barnum. This is on credit today. I'm a poor woman and I pay up my bills all at once, twice a year."

"Pa said no credit — that I was to take cash only," answered Phineas. "I'm sorry, but you've got a long credit column already, Mrs. Sweeney."

Finding that her first method of bluster did not work, the Widow began to coax. "Now you're a good boy and not raised for impudence. Haven't I got the nicest little calf only two weeks old that I was calculating on giving your pa in payment, if he'd continue my credit a while?"

"Is it an all-right calf?" asked the youthful storekeeper bluntly.

"Of course it's all right! It's as pretty as can be. But it's got a curious failing — an extra eye."

"Oh!" Joy gleamed in Phineas's own eyes. If he could only get hold of that calf for purposes of his own!

"Well, marm — " he began. Then he hesitated, the thought of the ready strap at the back of his mind, but decided he'd have to take a chance. "If you'll let me stop around tonight and see it when I close up store, I can let you have these things now."

The gratified widow agreed, warmed herself thoroughly at the stove, and then went on her way. Meanwhile, Phineas Barnum resolved inwardly to show off that three-eyed calf behind his father's barn for a penny a peep — or maybe he'd charge two cents. What a find for the show he was planning!

His next customer was a red-headed boy, younger than himself, who painfully lugged in two pecks of apples to be exchanged for potatoes. As he set the half-bushel basket down with a thump, a snake glided across the uneven, splintered floor toward the heat.

"Hi, help me get him, Phin! He must have got out of my pocket!" screeched Hiram Fletcher. Young Barnum recaptured the snake in a wink, and shut him up in a small dark box.

"Can you do tricks with him?" asked Phineas.

"Only caught him yesterday," said Hiram, surprised at the idea.

"Bring him around to my house Saturday afternoon. Meet me behind the barn. We'll have a circus," proposed Phineas in an excited whisper. He saw three farmers entering, bent on leisurely purchases and conversation. "There's lots of things I can tell you, but I've got to tend store now."

Hiram chuckled. "I'll see you later and I'll get Rafe and George and Buckle Ewing, too."

Farmers were likely to stay indefinitely on such a raw day. Phineas prepared for them by fetching out a couple of rickety wooden stools (the third could perch on the molasses barrel) and mending the fire. He brought out a jug of new cider.

"Hey, Phineas!" said the first farmer, Ezra Dean, a Yankee with rugged features and a long jaw. "Give me two pounds of tenpenny nails."

The busy storekeeper weighed them and was paid. "Two pennies more," he requested briskly.

Ezra dumped his weather-beaten purse out on the counter for inspection. Not a cent was in it.

"I'll give you a hopping bean instead, boy," he offered. "I know you like tricks."

"But does it really hop? Let me see for sure."

Ezra winked at the other men and produced a small brown object from his pocket. Placing it on the bottom of a broken cracker box, he carried it to the stove. Sure enough, the heat caused it to skip about here and there on the piece of board. The dance was fascinating. The farmers stood and watched, both interested and astonished.

"I haven't seen anything like that in a month of Sundays," said the oldest of the three, Mose Painter.

Phineas put the hopping bean carefully into his pocket.

"Thank you kindly," he said.

Ezra Dean joined his friends at the fire. The other two farmers, whom Barnum's son knew to be prosperous, would buy later and pay good greenbacks. They did not need to bargain except as a pastime.

As he waited on children, giggling schoolgirls, and shrewd New England housewives (for the store had filled up), Phineas caught snatches of conversation from the group of farmers around the stove. When the subject of local politics was exhausted, they turned to local horrors.

"Just try walking easy by that mill, at twilight, and you'll hear a high, queer voice, like a spirit's," one man said.

"Is that so! I didn't know the old mill was haunted."

"Well, 'tis. Steve Carter lost his watch chain when he was going by there, week or so ago."

"Time someone got to the bottom of this," said Mose Painter. Then the conversation drifted on to other matters.

The very same evening Phineas, who had been to see Widow Sweeney's three-eyed calf and agreed on a transfer, took a walk past the old Franklin mill on the village outskirts. He did not believe what the men at the store had said about the haunted mill. Anyway, he was more curious than afraid. In the moonlight the stone mill looked as peaceful as the stream that flowed beside it. Suddenly, from an upper window of the mill came easy, conversational tones.

"Good boy!" uttered a clipped, mocking voice, and then a dark shadow flew past him. Something with straw clinging to it jingled at his feet. Squatting on a stone, Phineas drew from his pocket a bit of bread and a cheese rind he kept for just such emergencies. The shadow drew nearer and perched on his finger. It was a raven!

329

"Good night," it said. "Have no-fear, no-fear."

Phineas caught the bird skillfully, slipped it into a bag he had brought, and picked up the object on the ground. It was nothing less than Steve Carter's gold watch chain! What a surprise that would be for Steve on Saturday!

A raven would be a great addition to the side shows. He had not yet been able to persuade Jabez Tutt, the man with the longest beard in the village, to be the Bearded Giant. But this raven was a find and he could teach it to talk in no time. It must have flown over from another township, where someone else had begun its education. He might rent a skull for it to perch on, if there was anyone about who had one handy. There was never going to be another exhibition like this one he planned. No, sir!

Next morning Phineas had Hiram and George, his brother and side-partner, take a brisk turn about Bethel. One went east, one west, until they had covered the town. In their hands they carried a pile of hand-printed advertisements that were stuck under front doors or pushed at anyone they happened to meet.

The Saturday Show

After three long days of storekeeping, Phineas had collected a goodly sum in his father's till as well as half a dozen barrels of fall pippins. Other transactions had taken place that made his heart light. Now it was Saturday noon. His father was still away, but at three o'clock he planned to close up the store until evening. His able partners were already at work preparing the place of entertainment behind the barn.

"Barnum's Saturday Show" was opening at four o'clock. Phineas had decided to charge a nickel for general admission and a penny apiece extra for special side shows. Of course the show couldn't begin until Phineas himself appeared.

The crowd that gathered back of Barnum's barn at four o'clock was enormous. At a rude turnstile made of two crossed laths stood Barnum's boy himself, hair tousled, face red with excitement.

"This way, ladies and gentlemen," he shouted, "to see the Three-Eyed Calf, the only specimen of its kind in captivity. Meet Jupiter, the domestic snake that snuggles up to you like an infant! See the Magic Bean, worked by Unseen Force, and Lupo the Raven, that talks and brings forth gold. Last chance, cash and tickets!"

"That boy of Barnum's has the gift of gab," said the tired mother of two fretting children. "First-rate showman! He'll make money or I miss my guess."

Farmers, curious to see, were driving up in carts and buggies, with children between their knees. Big boys were stumping in, leading younger brothers and sisters.

"This way, this way, to the calf. Put your money on the Three-Eyed Calf," called one of Barnum's assistants.

He was instantly reproved by his chief. "Say a lot more, Hi, about his unusual points — like this: 'The one and only calf in captivity that has an extra eye,' " corrected Phineas in ringing tones. Hiram cleared his throat and began again.

Meantime, a fearless brother younger than Phineas was riding Zeke, the runaway colt, round a chalked ring, sticking on his back in spite of frantic kickings and plungings. This feature, the only ten-cent one, was marvelously popular. When Bethel's crop of dimes had been taken in, the raven was produced.

"Step up here," announced the showman to late comers. "Plenty of room to stand. Step up!" Then, "What do you like best, Lupo?" he asked, holding up the raven.

"Gold," said Lupo, in a hoarse voice.

"What next to that?"

"Chain," croaked the raven.

"And then?"

"Gold chain."

"Now. Tell the gentleman whose watch chain you took that you are sorry."

"Sorry," croaked Lupo.

Steve Carter, eyes popping, was beckoned forward to receive his missing watch chain.

"I declare!" was all he could say.

As a final feature, the hopping bean began gamboling briskly on a table. Young Phineas had learned exactly how much heat to give it from his warm, perspiring palm.

Home-made doughnuts and cider were being offered to the still admiring crowd when hoofs were heard approaching briskly. Soon a tired mare came into view on the far side of the barn. In the buggy were the substantial shoulders of Pa Barnum, his wife by his side.

Barnum Senior's astonishment when he saw the gathering

on the lot back of his barn was followed by a grim expression about the jaw. That fool boy of his, who was so keen on freaks and shows, had gone and closed up the store (yes, it was shut and silent when he passed it), and lost the tide of the late Saturday afternoon trade. He could not help being secretly proud of his son's talents but he'd have to teach him a lesson for all that.

"Phineas," he called in tones to wake the dead, "you come here and stop this fooling."

Some little distance away, he seemed to see a familiar form, to hear a familiar voice. "Calf," it was saying.

Calf! Was it possible there was a new heifer? Excitedly, Barnum stopped the buggy, threw the reins to his wife, got out and stumped over to the circus enclosure.

"Nickel, please, Mister Barnum," requested the gatekeeper. Inwardly raging, Barnum paid it and continued his search.

"Excuse me, folks," he kept saying until suddenly, in a pen near him, he saw one of the finest little heifer calves. It was sound in wind and limb, the only defect being a curious third eye over the regular one on the left side.

Then father and son met face to face. Young Barnum's expression was as bland as cream.

"Hello, Pa," he said. "See the calf you got from the Widow Sweeney."

"How much did you give for it?" roared his father.

"Not a penny. It was a present in payment."

"Well! And what have you to say about closing the store and losing my Saturday afternoon trade?"

"I was going to reopen this evening," stated Phineas confidently, "and what I've taken in on entrances will make up for any loss. I've got a good sight of money in here, Pa, and it's all yours!" He gleefully rattled the contents of a tin can in his father's ears.

Parent looked at son with sudden added respect.

"You've not cheated anyone to get hold of these critters?" Barnum Senior indicated, in one sweeping gesture, the calf, the raven, the snake, and the colt. "I nearly stepped on that dratted snake," he exploded as it wiggled near his boots.

"No, Pa, I didn't cheat. When folks come in to celebrate, I like to show them a thing or two," Phineas confessed. "I only quit the store an hour ago."

His father scratched his head. "I always took it you had smartness in you," was his only comment, as he accepted the offered can.

Young Barnum looked triumphantly around. The crowd was scattering. His father had calmed down and was peering into this box and that pen to see what else he could see. But somehow the barn lot was not quite large enough for Phineas. Some day there must be a big white tent pegged down at the corners or maybe a hall. In his imagination such a hall swelled and grew bigger until he had it peopled with weird shapes. He'd like a family of dwarfs — a giant, too — and a voice that would fill space with its ringing music and make echoes come out of the air. Some day he'd have that, too.

Laura Benét

BABY RAINSTORM

ONE spring, a good many years back, Paul Bunyan had a logging camp on the headwaters of the River That Ran Sidewise. He'd had a profitable winter and the landings were jammed full of logs decked up and waiting for the spring floods to float them down to the mills.

Finally the weather turned warm and the snow started to melt. The big drive would be under way in a few more days. Then one morning the men woke up to find it raining. Now rain is not so unusual at that time of the year, but this was no ordinary rain. No, sir! For instead of coming down like ordinary rain, this rain came straight up. All over camp, as far as anyone could see, streams of big raindrops were squirting up out of the ground, sailing straight up in the air and disappearing into the clouds.

And with the rain came trouble. For, as anyone knows, almost all the rain in this country comes down, so of course houses are built to take care of that kind of rain, seldom giving the other kind a thought. And that was the case in

Ol' Paul's camp. The buildings all had tight roofs but the floors were made with wide cracks so that water and mud tracked in by the lumberjacks would run through to the ground below.

But now, with the rain coming up, the floors leaked like sieves and the water gathered on the ceilings and couldn't leak out. By the time the men woke up, the water was four feet deep on the under side of the ceiling of every bunkhouse in camp, and it was getting deeper every minute. As the men got up they had to duck their heads to keep from bumping into the water.

One of the loggers hotfooted it over to Paul's office to tell him about it.

"Paul!" he hollered when he could get his breath. "The rain is a-coming straight up this morning!"

"You mean it's a-coming up to rain, don't you?" Paul asked, as he hunted under his bunk for his socks. "Why don't you learn to say what you mean?"

"No, sir!" the lumberjack insisted. "I meant just what I said. This morning the rain is a-coming straight up out of the ground. You can take a look and see for yourself!"

Ol' Paul finally discovered that he already had his socks on because he'd never taken them off when he went to bed, so he put on his boots and tramped over to the window to see what was what. At first he couldn't believe his eyes. He put the window up to get a better look, and still he didn't believe what he saw. He tried looking out of first one eye and then the other. Then he got out his specs, which he usually didn't wear when anyone was around,

337

and clamped them on his nose, and went outside to have a good close look. But any way he looked at it, the rain was sure enough coming straight up.

So Ol' Paul and the lumberjack sat down together to think about it.

After a while the lumberjack spoke up. "Paul," said he, "a fellow is prepared for ordinary rain, for all his clothes are made to take care of it, if you ever noticed."

"How do you figure that?" Paul wanted to know.

"Well, a fellow's hat brim sticks out so the rain won't run down his collar much. And his coat overlaps his britches, and his britches overlap his boots. It's like being shingled, if you see what I mean."

"That's right," said Paul. "But where would you say that leaves us?"

"Well, when the rain comes up, instead of down, it falls straight up the legs of his britches, straight up under his coat, and straight up his sleeves. It's mighty, mighty uncomfortable. I wonder, now, if it wouldn't be possible to shingle a fellow upside down."

And then they sat and thought some more, since the big bear skin in the middle of Paul's floor kept the rain from hitting them as it came up.

Meanwhile, the lumberjacks over in the bunkhouses, and the stable hands and the mess hall boys were all in a very bad humor. The cooks were in a bad humor, too, but camp cooks are almost always that way, so nobody noticed any particular difference.

After a while, a delegation came to Ol' Paul Bunyan

338

and told him that he'd better do something about this business pretty soon or they'd all quit and go to work for his rival.

Ol' Paul assured them that he'd get to the bottom of the mystery as soon as possible, but pointed out to them that it would take time, since nothing like it had ever happened before. That being the case, there was of course nothing written in the books about how to deal with it. So he'd have to figure it all out by himself.

"Besides," he told them, "think of the stories you can tell in the towns this summer, about how you got your drive out in spite of the rain that fell straight up!"

But they were still mad and going to quit, so he saw he'd have to take measures pretty quick.

After quite a spell of unusually heavy thinking, he called for Johnny Inkslinger to quick make out an order to his favorite mail-order house for enough bumbershoots to make two apiece for all the men in camp.

"Bumbershoots?" Johnny asked. "What are bumbershoots?"

"Why, the things folks hold up over their heads when it's raining," said Paul. "I've seen pictures of them in the catalogues many a time."

"What you mean is umbrellas," said Johnny, who comes from up Boston way and always talks sort of special. "And besides," said he, "they will do no good in this emergency, because they are made for rain that falls down and this rain is undoubtedly coming straight up instead."

"You go on and do what I say," said Paul. "I'll figure

339

out a way to use them by the time I get them. Tell them this is a hustle-up order."

A couple of days later the bumbershoots came, two for every man in camp, and you should have heard the lumberjacks roar. No self-respecting lumberjack had ever been known to carry one of the sissy things and they weren't going to start it now. They might be all right for city dudes, but not for regular he-lumberjacks! No, sir! They'd quit first.

Ol' Paul went on helping Ole open the boxes and told the lumberjacks just to keep their shirts on a minute till they saw what he had in mind.

As fast as the bumbershoots were unpacked, the Little

Chore Boy opened them up and Ol' Paul took his jack-knife and cut the handles off short inside and fastened on a couple of snowshoe loops, instead. When he had them all fixed up, he had Johnnie call the roll. As each logger came up, Paul handed him a couple of the remodeled bumbershoots and told him to slip his feet into the loops.

The first men were a mite shy about the business, but after they had put them on and straddled off, as if they were wearing snowshoes, they found that the bumbershoots did keep the rain from coming up their pants-legs. And from then on the men pushed and hollered for the men ahead to hurry up so they could get theirs.

"See there," said Ol' Paul, "I guess I knew what I was

341

doing. I reckon there isn't anything sissy about wearing bumbershoots on your feet. And, anyway, we'll call them bumbershoes from now on, just to be sure!"

The men all cheered again, and decided not to quit camp after all, though the rain was still coming straight up.

THE LOST BABY

The next morning a friendly Indian chief came tearing into camp, wanting to see Paul. He told Ol' Paul that when he and another Indian were out hunting the day before, they had camped by the mouth of a cave out on the prairie. After they had eaten their supper, they decided to explore this cave, so they took along some pine knots for torches, and started out. They went back through the narrow twisting passages for about half a mile, as near as they could judge, when all of a sudden they heard the most dreadful noise they'd ever laid an ear next to. They didn't stop to argue, but tore out of there as fast as they could. They figured that by going in there they had made the Great Spirit mad, and that he was hollering at them. So now the Indian wanted Paul to see if he could talk to the Great Spirit and make him quiet down.

Ol' Paul was curious, but from what the chief told him, he knew the cave was too small for him to get into, so he sat still and thought for a spell. Finally, he allowed as how maybe two men listening together could listen far enough back to hear the noise from the mouth of the cave. That sounded like a good idea, but the Indian was too scared to go back, so Paul called Chris Crosshaul to go along instead.

The cave wasn't hard to find, and when they got there they both listened as hard as they could and, sure enough, they just about heard the noise. But when they tried listening separately they couldn't hear a sound. (It's a well-known fact that two men listening together can hear twice as far as one man listening alone.)

For a while Paul listened to the rumpus he could hear going on back in the cave, and a very curious sound it was, too. It was sort of mixed up with whimpering and whining like a lost puppy, and dribbling, splashing sounds, and a sort of pattering, and, now and again, a hollow booming such as lightning might make if shut up in a cellar.

After a spell of especially hard listening that left them both red in the face and out of breath, Paul turned to Chris and said, "Chris, that's nothing in the wide world but a baby rainstorm that's got himself lost back in this here cave, and now he's bellowing for his mother!"

"You don't say," said Chris, doubtful-like.

"Yes, sir!" said Paul. "And by looking at my pocket compass I've discovered that the noise is a-coming from right under our lumber camp. The way I figure it, that little fellow got separated from the rest of the herd and got in here by mistake a while back. Now, he's lost and scared. You just heard him whimpering and thundering his heart out back in there. Chances are he's got all upset in the dark and is raining straight up instead of down and doesn't know it. We've got to get him out."

"How can we do that?" said Chris Crosshaul.

"Well, the way I see it," said Ol' Paul, "the only way to get that critter out of there is to call him out. It's a cinch we can't drag him out because there is no way to catch hold of a critter like that. And nobody ever had any luck trying to chase a rainstorm anywhere that I ever heard tell about."

"I reckon you're right at that, Paul," said Chris, "but I never heard of anyone that can call a rainstorm, either."

"That's the beauty of the whole thing," said Paul. "We'll be the first ones ever to do such a thing."

"Just how do you figure to go about it?" Chris wanted to know. "You don't mean you can holler like a rainstorm, do you?"

"Not right now, I can't," said Paul. "But I figure I can soon learn how. You see, I know a fellow in Kansas City that will rent all kinds of disguises. I'll get him to disguise me to look like a rainstorm. Then I'll go out and live with a tribe of them and learn their language. It should be simple enough, shouldn't it?"

And that's just what he did. He got all dressed up in a rainstorm suit till you wouldn't have known him. Then he went out into Iowa where most of the rainstorms summered. He fell in with a big tribe of them, and his disguise was so perfect that they just figured he was a strange rainstorm, maybe blown up from Texas way, and they invited him to stay with them as long as he liked.

He had a mighty fine time all summer, helping the rainstorms to soak open-air political meetings and the like, although probably he took an unfair advantage at times. He always managed to get the rainstorms to rain on people he didn't want elected, and kept them away from the rallies of people he liked.

But, anyway, late in the summer he came back, and just to show off, he was always throwing rainstorm words into his talk, till the lumberjacks scarcely knew what he was talking about. Then one day he went to the mouth of the cave where the rainstorm was. Getting down on his hands and knees, he put his face up close to the cave and imitated the cry a mother rainstorm makes when she is calling her young ones.

As soon as he did that, the noise and thundering and blubbering inside the cave stopped at once. There wasn't a sound to be heard, and the rain, for the first time all summer, stopped coming up around camp.

"See that?" said Paul, with a big grin. And then he hollered the rainstorm holler again, and that little rainstorm came tearing out of the cave as if he'd been sent for. He was just a little fellow compared to what some rainstorms are, and a mite puny-looking from being shut in the dark for so long. He jumped into Ol' Paul's arms and licked his face like an excited puppy dog.

Ol' Paul petted him and talked to him soothingly till he quieted down, then sent him off down to Iowa where the rest of the rainstorms are. The last we saw of him he was just a little cloud over in the next county, all decked out with rainbows, he was so tickled.

Glen Rounds

BUFFALO BILL

I say! what a thrill!
Here's Buffalo Bill,
The King of the Cowboys in valor and skill,
With his fringes of leather, his cowpuncher's hat,
His lasso and pistols and boots and all that!
　Stout-hearted and hairy,
　With confidence airy,
He slew the wild buffalo roaming the prairie,
And played the chief part in exciting events
Enacted around the Red Indian tents,
　And when the news came,
　As part of the game,
That the Redskins had set his log-cabin aflame,
　He rode without pause
　To put down the cause
'Mid the yelling of braves and the squawking of squaws.
　He fought a lot more
　As Scoutmaster for
The troops of the North in the Great Civil War,
And America's mail through the land was conveyed
By his Pony Express ere the railway was made.
　And I say! what a thrill
　When Buffalo Bill,
Who, agog for adventure, could never keep still,
Got up a fine circus, to show every one

How the Redskin-and-buffalo business was done!
  What glee and what glory
  To see his life-story
Presented in episodes pleasantly gory,
With whips and with scalps that were cracked with a will
By breakneck, unbeatable Buffalo Bill!

              Eleanor and *Herbert Farjeon*

347

A ROOTABAGA STORY

GIMME THE AX lived in a house where everything
is the same as it always was.

"The chimney sits on top of the house and lets the
smoke out," said Gimme the Ax. "The doorknobs open
the doors. The windows are always either open or shut.
We are always either upstairs or downstairs in this house.
Everything is the same as it always was."

So he decided to let his children name themselves.

"The first words they speak as soon as they learn to make words shall be their names," he said. "They shall name themselves."

When the first boy came to the house of Gimme the Ax, he was named Please Gimme. When the first girl came she was named Ax Me No Questions.

And both children had the shadows of valleys by night in their eyes and the lights of early morning, when the sun is coming up, on their foreheads.

And the hair on top of their heads was a dark wild grass. And they loved to turn the doorknobs, and run out to have the wind comb their hair and touch their eyes and put its six soft fingers on their foreheads.

And then, because no more boys came and no more girls came, Gimme the Ax said to himself, "My first boy is my last, and my last girl is my first, and they picked their names themselves."

Please Gimme grew up and his ears got longer. Ax Me No Questions grew up and her ears got longer. And they kept on living in the house where everything is the same as it always was. They learned to say just as their father said, "The chimney sits on top of the house and lets the smoke out. The doorknobs open the doors. The windows are always either open or shut. We are always either upstairs or downstairs. Everything is the same as it always was."

After a while they began asking each other in the cool of the evening after they had eggs for breakfast in the morning, "Who's who? How much? And what's the answer?"

"It is too much to be too long anywhere," said the tough old man, Gimme the Ax.

And Please Gimme and Ax Me No Questions, the tough son and the tough daughter of Gimme the Ax, answered their father, "It is too much to be too long anywhere."

So they sold everything they had, — pigs, pastures, pepper pickers, pitchforks, — everything except their ragbags and a few extras.

When their neighbors saw them selling everything they had, the different neighbors said, "They are going to Kansas, to Kokomo, to Canada, to Kankakee, to Kalamazoo, to Kamchatka, to the Chattahoochee."

One little sniffer, with his eyes half shut and a mitten on his nose, laughed in his hat five ways and said, "They are going to the moon, and when they get there, they will find everything is the same as it always was."

All the spot-cash money he got for selling everything, — pigs, pastures, pepper pickers, pitchforks, — Gimme the Ax put in a ragbag and slung on his back like a rag picker going home.

Then he took Please Gimme, his oldest and youngest and only son, and Ax Me No Questions, his oldest and youngest and only daughter, and went to the railway station.

The ticket agent was sitting at the window selling railroad tickets the same as always.

"Do you wish a ticket to go away and come back or do you wish a ticket to go away and never come back?" the ticket agent asked, wiping sleep out of his eyes.

"We wish a ticket to ride where the railroad tracks run off into the sky and never come back. Send us far as the railroad rails go, and then forty ways farther yet," was the reply of Gimme the Ax.

"So far? So early? So soon?" asked the ticket agent, wiping more sleep out of his eyes. "Then I will give you a new ticket. It blew in. It is a long slick yellow-leather ticket with a blue spanch across it."

Gimme the Ax thanked the ticket agent once, thanked the ticket agent twice, and then instead of thanking the ticket agent three times, he opened the ragbag and took out all the spot-cash money he got for selling everything, — pigs, pastures, pepper pickers, pitchforks, — and paid the spot-cash money to the ticket agent.

Before he put it in his pocket he looked once, twice, three times at the long yellow-leather slab ticket with a blue spanch across it.

Then, with Please Gimme and Ax Me No Questions, he got on the railroad train, showed the conductor his ticket, and they started to ride to where the railroad tracks run off into the blue sky and then forty ways farther yet. The train ran on and on. It came to the place where the railroad tracks run off into the blue sky. And it ran on and on, chick chick-a-chick, chick-a-chick, chick-a-chick.

Sometimes the engineer hooted and tooted the whistle. Sometimes the fireman rang the bell. Sometimes the open-and-shut of the steam hog's nose choked and spit pfisty-pfoost, pfisty-pfoost, pfisty-pfoost. But no matter what happened to the whistle and the bell and the steam hog, the train ran on and on to where the railroad tracks run off into the blue sky. And then it ran on and on more and more.

Sometimes Gimme the Ax looked in his pocket, put his fingers in, and took out the yellow-leather slab ticket with the blue spanch across it.

"Not even the kings of Egypt with all their climbing camels, and all their speedy, spotted, lucky lizards, ever had a ride like this," he said to his children.

Then something happened. They met another train running on the same track. One train was going one way. The other was going the other way. They met. They passed each other.

"What was it? What happened?" the children asked their father.

"One train went over, the other train went under," he answered. "This is the Over and Under Country. Nobody gets out of the way of anybody else. They either go over or under."

Next they came to the country of the balloon pickers. Hanging down from the sky on strings so fine the eye could not see them at first, was the balloon crop of that summer. The sky was thick with balloons. Red, blue, yellow balloons — white, purple, and orange balloons — peach, watermelon, and potato balloons — rye-loaf and wheat-loaf balloons — link-sausage and pork-chop balloons — they floated and filled the sky.

The balloon pickers were walking on high stilts picking balloons. Each picker had his own stilts, long or short.

For picking balloons near the ground he had short stilts.
If he wanted to pick far and high he walked on a far and
high pair of stilts.

Baby pickers on baby stilts were picking baby balloons.
When they fell off the stilts the handful of balloons they
were holding kept them in the air till they got their feet
into the stilts again.

"Who is that away up there in the sky climbing like a

353

bird in the morning?" Ax Me No Questions asked her father.

"He was singing too happy," replied the father. "The songs came out of his neck and made him so light that balloons pulled him off his stilts."

"Will he ever come down again back to his own people?"

"Yes, his heart will get heavy when his songs are all gone. Then he will drop down to his stilts again."

The train was running on and on. The engineer hooted and tooted the whistle when he felt like it. The fireman rang the bell when he felt that way. And sometimes the open-and-shut of the steam hog had to go pfisty-pfoost, pfisty-pfoost.

"Next is the country where the circus clowns come from," said Gimme the Ax to his son and daughter. "Keep your eyes open."

They did keep their eyes open. They saw cities with ovens, long and short ovens, fat stubby ovens, lean lank ovens, all for baking either long or short clowns, or fat and stubby, or lean and lank clowns.

After each clown was baked in the oven, it was taken out in the sunshine and put up to stand like a big white doll with a red mouth leaning against the fence.

Two men came along to each baked clown standing still like a doll. One man threw a bucket of white fire over it. The second man pumped a wind pump with a living red wind through the red mouth.

The clown rubbed his eyes, opened his mouth, twisted

his neck, wiggled his ears, wriggled his toes, jumped away from the fence, and began turning handsprings, cartwheels, somersaults, and flipflops in the sawdust ring near the fence.

"The next we come to is the Rootabaga Country where the big city is the Village of Liver-and-Onions," said Gimme the Ax, looking again in his pocket to be sure he had the long slick yellow-leather slab ticket with a blue spanch across it.

The train ran on and on till it stopped running straight and began running in zigzags like one letter Z put next to another Z and the next and the next.

The tracks and the rails and the ties and the spikes under the train all stopped being straight and changed to zigzags like one letter Z and another letter Z put next after the other.

"It seems like we go half way and then back up," said Ax Me No Questions.

"Look out of the window and see if the pigs have bibs on," said Gimme the Ax. "If the pigs are wearing bibs, then this is the Rootabaga Country."

And they looked out of the zigzagging windows of the zigzagging cars and the first pigs they saw had bibs on. And the next pigs and the next pigs they saw all had bibs on.

The checker pigs had checker bibs on. The striped pigs had striped bibs on. And the polka-dot pigs had polka-dot bibs on.

"Who fixes it for the pigs to have bibs on?" Please Gimme asked his father.

"The fathers and mothers fix it," answered Gimme the Ax. "The checker pigs have checker fathers and mothers. The striped pigs have striped fathers and mothers. And the polka-dot pigs have polka-dot fathers and mothers."

And the train went zigzagging on and on, running on the tracks and the rails and the spikes which were all zigzag like the letter Z and the letter Z.

And after a while the train zigzagged on into the Village of Liver-and-Onions, known as the biggest city in the big, big Rootabaga Country.

And so if you are going to the Rootabaga Country, you will know when you get there because the railroad tracks change from straight to zigzag, the pigs have bibs on, and it is the fathers and mothers who fix it.

And if you start to go to that country, remember first you must sell everything you have, — pigs, pastures, pepper pickers, pitchforks, — put the spot-cash money in a ragbag, and go to the railroad station and ask the ticket agent for a long slick yellow-leather slab ticket with a blue spanch across it.

And you mustn't be surprised if the ticket agent wipes sleep from his eyes and asks, "So far? So early? So soon?"

Carl Sandburg

THE RUM TUM TUGGER

THE Rum Tum Tugger is a Curious Cat:
If you offer him pheasant, he would rather have grouse.
If you put him in a house, he would much prefer a flat;
If you put him in a flat, then he'd rather have a house.
If you set him on a mouse, then he only wants a rat;
If you set him on a rat, then he'd rather chase a mouse.
Yes, the Rum Tum Tugger is a Curious Cat —
   And there isn't any call for me to shout it;
     For he will do
     As he do do
       And there's no doing anything about it!

The Rum Tum Tugger is a terrible bore:
When you let him in, then he wants to be out;
He's always on the wrong side of every door,
And as soon as he's at home, then he'd like to get about.

He likes to lie in the bureau drawer,
But he makes such a fuss if he can't get out.
Yes, the Rum Tum Tugger is a Curious Cat —
    And it isn't any use for you to doubt it;
        For he will do
        As he do do
            And there's no doing anything about it!

The Rum Tum Tugger is a curious beast:
His disobliging ways are a matter of habit.
If you offer him fish, then he always wants a feast;
When there isn't any fish, then he won't eat rabbit.
If you offer him cream, then he sniffs and sneers,
For he only likes what he finds for himself;
So you'll catch him in it right up to the ears,
If you put it away on the larder shelf.
The Rum Tum Tugger is artful and knowing;
The Rum Tum Tugger doesn't care for a cuddle,
But he'll leap on your lap in the middle of your sewing,
For there's nothing he enjoys like a horrible muddle.
Yes, the Rum Tum Tugger is a Curious Cat —
    And there isn't any need for me to spout it;
        For he will do
        As he do do
            And there's no doing anything about it!

                                    T. S. Eliot

INDIANS AND PIONEERS

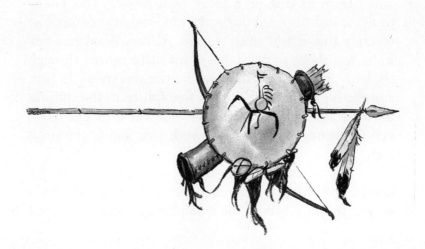

WAUKEWA'S EAGLE

ONE day, when the Indian boy Waukewa was hunting along the mountainside, he found a young eagle with a broken wing lying at the base of a cliff. The bird had fallen from its nest on a ledge high above. Too young to fly, it had fluttered down the cliff and injured itself so severely that it was likely to die. When Waukewa saw it, he was about to drive one of his sharp arrows through the body, for the passion of the hunter was strong in him, and the eagle plunders many a fine fish from the Indian's drying-frame. But a gentler impulse came to him as he saw the young bird quivering with pain and fright at his feet.

He slowly unbent his bow, put the arrow back in his quiver, and stooped over the panting eaglet. For fully a minute the wild eyes of the wounded bird and the eyes of the Indian boy, growing gentler and softer as he gazed, looked into one another. Then the struggling and panting of the young eagle ceased. The wild, frightened look passed out of its eyes, and it allowed Waukewa to pass his hand gently over its ruffled and bedraggled feathers. The fierce instinct to fight, to defend its life, yielded to the tenderness and pity expressed in the boy's eyes. From that moment, Waukewa and the eagle were friends.

Waukewa went slowly home to his father's lodge, bearing the wounded eaglet in his arms. He carried it so gently that the broken wing gave no twinge of pain, and the bird lay perfectly still, never offering to strike with its sharp beak the hands that clasped it.

Warming some water over the fire at the lodge, Waukewa bathed the broken wing of the eagle and bound it up with soft strips of skin. Then he made a nest of ferns and grass inside the lodge, and laid the bird in it. The boy's mother looked on with shining eyes. Her heart was very tender. From girlhood she had loved all the creatures of the woods, and it pleased her to see some of her own gentle spirit waking in the boy.

When Waukewa's father returned from hunting, he would have caught up the young eagle and wrung its neck. But the boy pleaded with him so eagerly, stooping over the captive and defending it with his small hands, that the stern warrior laughed and called him "little squaw-heart."

"Keep it, then," he said, "and nurse it until it is well. But then you must let it go, for we will not raise up a thief in the lodges."

361

So Waukewa promised that when the eagle's wing was healed and the eaglet had grown so that it could fly, he would carry it forth and give it its freedom.

It was a month — or, as the Indians say, a moon — before the young eagle's wing had fully mended and the bird was old enough and strong enough to fly. In the meantime Waukewa cared for it and fed it daily, and the friendship between the boy and the bird grew very strong.

At last the time came when the willing captive must be freed. So Waukewa carried it far away from the Indian lodges, where none of the young braves might see it hovering over and be tempted to shoot their arrows at it, and there he let it go.

The young eagle rose toward the sky in great circles, rejoicing in its freedom and its strange, new power of flight. But when Waukewa began to move away from the spot, it came swooping down again; and all day long it followed him through the woods as he hunted. At dusk, when Waukewa turned back toward the Indian lodges, the eagle would have accompanied him, but the boy suddenly slipped into a hollow tree and hid. After a long time the eagle stopped sweeping about in search of him and flew slowly and sadly away.

Summer passed, and then winter, and spring came again, with its flowers and birds and swarming fish in the lakes and streams. Then it was that all the Indians, old and young, braves and squaws, pushed their light canoes out from shore, and with spear and hook waged pleasant war against the salmon and the red-spotted trout. After winter's long imprisonment, it was such joy to feel the sunshine and the warm wind and to catch savory fish to take the place of dried meats and corn!

Above the great falls of the Apahoqui, the salmon sported in the cool current, darting under the lee of the rocks and leaping full length in the clear spring air. Nowhere else were such salmon to be speared as those which lay among the riffles at the head of the Apahoqui rapids. But only the most daring braves ventured to seek them there, for the current was strong. Should a light canoe once pass the danger point and get caught in the rush of the rapids, nothing could save it from going over the roaring falls.

Very early in the morning of a clear April day, just as the sun was rising splendidly over the mountains, Waukewa launched his canoe a half mile above the rapids of the Apahoqui, and floated downward, spear in hand, among the salmon riffles. He was the only one of the Indian lads who dared fish above the falls. But he had been there often, and never yet had his watchful eye and his strong paddle allowed the current to carry his canoe beyond the danger point. This morning he was alone on the river, for he had risen long before daylight to be first at the sport.

The riffles were full of salmon, big, lusty fellows, who glided about the canoe on every side in an endless silver stream. Waukewa plunged his spear right and left, and tossed one glittering victim after another into the bark canoe. So absorbed in the sport was he that for once he did not notice when the canoe began to glide more swiftly among the rocks. But suddenly he looked up, caught his paddle, and dipped it wildly in the swirling water. The canoe swung sidewise, shivered, held its own against the torrent, and then slowly, inch by inch, began to creep upstream toward the shore. Suddenly there was a loud snap, and the paddle parted in the boy's hands, broken just above the blade. Waukewa gave a cry of despair. Then he bent to the gunwale of his canoe and with the shattered blade fought desperately against the current. But it was useless. The racing torrent swept him downward. The hungry falls roared in his ears.

Then the Indian boy knelt calmly upright in the canoe, facing the mist of the falls, and folded his arms. His young face was stern and lofty. He had lived like a brave. Now he would die like one.

Faster and faster sped the doomed canoe toward the great cataract. The black rocks glided away on either side like phantoms. The roar of the terrible waters became like thunder in the boy's ears. But still he gazed calmly and sternly ahead, facing his fate as a brave Indian should. At last he began to chant the death-song which he had learned from the older braves. In a few moments all would be over. But he would come before the Great Spirit with a fearless hymn upon his lips.

Suddenly a shadow fell across the canoe. Waukewa

lifted his eyes and saw a great eagle hovering over, with dangling legs, and a spread of wings that blotted out the sun. Once more the eyes of the Indian boy and the eagle met.

With a glad cry the Indian boy stood up in his canoe, and the eagle hovered lower. As the canoe tossed up on that great swelling wave that climbs to the cataract's edge, the boy lifted his hands and caught the legs of the eagle. The next moment he looked down into the awful gulf of waters. The canoe was snatched from beneath him and plunged down the black wall of the cataract. He and the struggling eagle floated outward and downwards through the cloud of mist.

The cataract roared terribly, like a wild beast robbed of its prey. The spray beat and blinded. The air rushed upward as they fell. But the eagle struggled on with his burden. He fought his way out of the mist and the flying spray. His great wings threshed the air with a whistling sound. Down, down they sank, the boy and the eagle, but ever farther from the precipice of water and the boiling whirlpool below. At length, with a fluttering plunge, the eagle dropped on a sand-bar below the whirlpool. He and the Indian boy lay there a minute, breathless and exhausted.

Then the eagle slowly lifted himself, took the air under his free wings, and soared away, while the Indian boy knelt on the sand, with shining eyes following the great bird till he faded into the gray of the cliffs.

James Buckham

THE DEER–STAR

HEAR now a tale of the deer-star,
    Tale of the days agone,
When a youth rose up for the hunting
    In the bluish light of dawn —
Rose up for the red deer hunting,
    And what should a hunter do
Who has never an arrow feathered,
    Nor a bow strung taut and true?
The women laughed from the doorways, the maidens
    mocked at the spring;
For thus to be slack at the hunting is ever a shameful thing.
The old men nodded and muttered, but the youth spoke
    up with a frown:
"If I have no gear for the hunting, I will run the red deer
    down."

He is off by the hills of the morning,
    By the dim, untrodden ways;
In the clean, wet, windy marshes
    He has startled the deer agraze;
Then a buck of ten-point antlers
    Streams out from the fleeing herd,
And the youth is apt to the running
    As the tongue to the spoken word.

They have gone by the broken ridges, by mesa and hill and
  swale,
Not once did the red deer falter, nor the feet of the runner fail;
So lightly they trod on the lupines that scarce were the
  flower-stalks bent,
And over the tops of the dusky sage the wind of their
  running went.

> They have gone by the painted desert,
>   Where the dawn mists lie uncurled,
> And over the purple ranges
>   On the outer rim of the world.
> The people shout from the village,
>   And the sun gets up to spy
> The royal deer and the runner,
>   Clear shining in the sky.

And ever the hunter watches for the rising of that star
When he comes by the summer mountains where the
  haunts of the red deer are,
When he comes by the morning meadows where the
  young of the red deer hide;
He fares him forth to the hunting while the deer and the
  runner hide.

Mary Austin

LETTER FROM QUEBEC

August 31, 1609

YOU cried when I came away from old Brouage, but I am sure you will be happy when you see this letter. It is written just to you and is going to be carried across the wide ocean in a great ship for nothing else but to please my little brother Guillaume. I know that you cannot write me an answer yet, but never mind. Learn as fast as you can, and it will not be long before you can send a letter to the Rock.

The Rock is a great cliff, higher than the highest steeple that you ever saw. It would not be very easy to climb it if the rain had not washed out a rough sort of path. Some day that cliff will have a fort on it, the Sieur de Champlain says, and there will be a town, or at any rate a village. It does not look much like even a village now, though the Indians come from away back in the forest to see the wonderful houses that we have built.

We did not come here in a day. We were on the ocean six long weeks before we caught even a glimpse of land. That was Newfoundland. It was not level and bright and sunny like Brouage. First, it was nothing but a fog bank. Then all of a sudden the fog swept away, and there were tall cliffs of dark red rock. It looked dark and gloomy, and I was glad we were not to stop there.

We sailed on past big islands and little islands. One

looked just like a whale. Another was higher than a
church steeple.

We heard this island before we saw it. What do you
think of that? We heard shrieking and squalling and
screaming and screeching. They say there are demons on
some of these islands. We could not see anything, but
after the fog blew away, there was an immense rock. Two
great passageways were pierced through it at the base
large enough for a boat to pass.

The noises did not stop, but we found out what made
them. It was nothing but birds, and there was not a demon
to be seen. The gulls live on one end of the rock, and the
cormorants on the other. They quarrel every little while,
and then they fight and scream and squawk and make all
the rest of the noises. They kept up the din as long as
we could see them or hear them.

We passed the pierced rock and sailed on and on into the mighty Saint Lawrence River. After a while we landed at a point that the Indians call Tadousac. Then we were surprised, for two ships were in the harbor. Captain Pontgravé was on board one of them. He had come to buy furs.

I know you are wondering of whom he bought them. He bought them of real Indians. They were living in wigwams made of poles fastened together at the top and covered with bark. They hunt in the winter and get beautiful furs. They are glad to sell them for such things as knives, hatchets, blankets, and beads. In addition, they buy furs from tribes that live far to the northward and bring them down in little birch-bark canoes. Did you ever see a waterfly skimming over the top of the water? That is the way the canoes look when they are not loaded.

The dark waters of the Saguenay made a broad black mark where they entered the blue Saint Lawrence, but beyond that the river was bright and sunny. The big white whales were rolling and tumbling about, and their backs flashed in the sunshine. They have plenty of room to roll. If there were thousands and thousands more of them, they would not be crowded, the river is so wide.

When the last day of June came, we left Tadousac and sailed on up the Saint Lawrence toward the place where our settlement was to be. There were miles and miles of forests, and once in a while a bright little meadow all fresh and green in the sunshine. There was a beautiful waterfall, too. At first it looked like a white ribbon floating down over the cliff. When we came nearer, we saw that it was really a cataract. The sun was shining on the foam at the foot of the fall, and it looked as if there were a whole gulf full of rainbows.

About three miles up the river was something we had come a long way to see. We expected to see it all winter and perhaps much longer, but we stared as if we should never have another chance. It was big, ever so much bigger than the cathedral you saw in Paris. It was gray, but when the sun suddenly broke through a cloud and shone upon it, it was warm and bright and glowing. Can you guess what it was? It was the Rock. You like to hear stories of giants, my Guillaume, and if you had seen this, I am sure you would have fancied that the biggest giant in all the world had pushed his great shoulder out into the river.

Now, Guillaume, if you had been the Governor, what would you have done first? You would have said, "I must build a house to keep me from the rain and the cold." That is exactly what the Governor did. He said, "Here is a fine strip of land close to the river. The cliff is behind it, and that will keep off some of the coldest winds. See how rich the ground looks and how finely the walnut trees are growing! Here is the place for our houses."

The Saint Lawrence is so large that there must be a great many rivers flowing into it, or maybe there is a great lake. If we follow up the river and find that there is no great lake, but that it rises somewhere in the mountains, then we may discover that from another little spring a brook flows in the opposite direction and that this by and by becomes a river and empties into the water off the coast of China. Then France can trade with China, and no other nation will be able to do that because we shall have the shortest way. The Sieur de Champlain would like to find that way, of course.

There are two other things that he wants to do quite as much. He does not care a very great deal to be rich, but he does care to found a village that will sometime become a city, and he cares to teach the Indians about God. I heard him say once that it was greater to save one soul than to found an empire. He hopes to be friends with the Indians about here, not only so he can trade with them, but so he can teach them to be good Christians.

I am sure that you know what we did next as well as I do. We went ashore and began to build our houses on the strip of land between the cliff and the river. You would have liked to see the work go on, I know, for everyone was as busy as he could be. The Governor looked about and chose what he thought was the best place for the houses. Then we all set to work to cut down the trees and clear the ground. The cellars were marked out and some of the men began to dig. Others went to the base of the cliff for stone. They did not have to break it off, for quantities of it had fallen, and it was already broken into pieces of all shapes and sizes. We wanted beams and planks, of course. I know well how to use an ax and a saw, so I helped in that part of the work.

I wish you could see the houses we built. There are

three besides a storehouse. In one house are the guns and powder and cannon balls. That has a sun-dial on the roof. In the second house is the blacksmith's forge, and in the third is the Governor's room. That is on the ground floor. A gallery runs around the second floor.

There is a palisade around the buildings and a moat fifteen feet wide and six feet deep. It has a drawbridge, and if you should come up to the gate some morning and say, "If you please, I want to come in," the man on guard would ask, "Are you a friend or an enemy?"

"I am a friend," you would reply. Then he would pull the ropes, down would go the drawbridge, and you would walk across the moat as easily as if you were crossing a floor. But now suppose you were an enemy — the bridge would stay up, and unless you could jump more than fifteen feet, you could not come to the door. You would not have a pleasant time waiting, either, for we have three cannon and one at least would be aimed right at you. Then I think you would say, "Please excuse me. I don't want to come in. I'd much rather run away."

There is one thing more which I haven't told you, and it is that we have a dovecot. It is so tall and slender that it looks like a little tower. There's another pleasant thing, and that is the Governor's garden. He made one just beyond the moat. He loves flowers, and then, too, he wanted to try different kinds of seeds to find out which will grow here. We planted much more than just a garden, for we sowed wheat and rye and set out some grapevines that we brought with us.

The Indians thought the buildings were wonderful. They came from a long way off to see what amazing houses had been put up at "Kebec." That is what they call the place, because the river narrows here, and "kebec" means a narrowing.

Some of the Indians built their wigwams just outside our palisade and went to work. What do you suppose red men do when they work? In this case, they caught eels and smoked them and dried them. Then, when they thought they had enough eels to live on for a month or two, they went off into the forest to hunt beaver and other animals whose furs they could sell. They asked Governor Champlain if he would take care of their eels for them while they were on the hunt. He said yes, and they went away off and were gone a good many weeks. Captain Pontgravé went away, too, for he had a good shipload of skins, and he sailed home to sell them for the Company.

Now, little brother, how should you have liked to be in our wooden castle, knowing that the ship had gone back to France, and you must stay where you were till it came again?

We had enough to eat, though there was none too much. We cut great piles of wood and brought it in, and we made the houses as tight and warm as we could. Then there was nothing for us to do but wait for the spring.

One thing you would have liked to see, and that was the forests before the snows came. The trees were all aglow with bright colors, much brighter and more beautiful than they ever are in France. Some were deep, dark red; some were blazing scarlet; some were almost purple; and some of the maples and birches were of such a golden yellow that they looked as if they were great masses of sunshine.

It would not have seemed half so gloomy if we could have kept the bright leaves all winter, but in a little while they all fell off. Then the snow began to come. Everything was white with it except the river, and that was black and cold.

We shivered, you may be sure, in spite of the great fires that we kept up. We burned logs so big that sometimes even two strong men could not bring them in without help. The wind blew in through every tiny crack, even through the thick boards, we fancied.

What did we do, my Guillaume, all those long days? We looked our guns over and rubbed them again and again. We melted lead and made bullets. The blacksmith examined every spade and hoe and shovel and put in order each one that was the least bit broken. We set traps for foxes. We made our meals last as long as we could. We slept, we played games, we talked about home, and we told stories.

The Sieur de Champlain did everything for us that a man could do. He was always cheery and good-natured. He kept the best of provisions put away, and when we were all feeling as if we should never see our own country again, he would give us something a little better than our everyday fare.

One day when it was fearfully cold, he told us about trying to found a colony on Saint Croix Island five years ago.

"This is nothing," he said, though he was shivering, "compared with Saint Croix Island. Here we have big fires with plenty of wood. We don't have to drink cider in chunks as we did there because we couldn't have fire enough to melt it. Just fancy how it would seem if over across the river there was a great forest and you were perishing with cold for the lack of a little wood. The river at Saint Croix was full of great cakes of ice. They were so heavy and came down so fast that no boat could have lived in it for a moment any more than it could live in the Saint Lawrence today."

He looked toward the river. Then he started, scraped off the frost from the windows to see more clearly, and cried, "See! They are trying to cross!"

We all rushed to the windows. The river was not frozen over then, but it was full from shore to shore with masses of ice pitching about. On the farther shore we could see some Indians getting into their canoes.

"They are mad," someone cried. "No boat could live there!"

The poor people were in the canoes and were paddling for their lives. The squaws and the children were huddled together in the bottom of the boats. Some of the men were trying to push away the cakes of ice with poles and others were paddling whenever there was a bit of water in which to paddle.

There was nothing to be done but to watch for the moment when they would be caught between the heavy cakes of ice and crushed. The men pushed with all their might, but they might as well have pushed against the Rock itself. We were gazing so eagerly that we almost fancied we could hear the sound when the canoes were crushed. In a moment more they were ground into bits and were gone.

But where do you think the people were, Guillaume? Not one went down with the canoes. They all jumped upon a monstrous cake of ice and were saved from that death. Some of the men still had their paddles, but they were of no use. Some had their poles, but only a giant would have been strong enough to thrust away the masses of ice that were coming down upon them.

We all hurried to the shore, and there we could hear them wail and lament. A little farther up the river we saw a thick sheet of ice sweeping down upon them. "That will carry them under," someone said, but it did not. I think the good God himself must have helped them. The sheet of ice struck the cake on which the Indians sat crouched together moaning, but it gave such a blow that the cake whirled around and was driven toward our shore.

We helped the poor people up the bank and brought them to the fort and gave them some bread and beans. You never saw anyone so thin in your life. They were so weak that they could hardly stand. I don't see how the squaws ever carried their little children and made such leaps from the canoes to the cake of ice. It must have been because they were starving, and their only hope was that, if they could get to us, we would give them food.

But I have not told you the hardest, saddest part of the winter's story. That was the sickness which came down upon us. There were twenty-eight of us in the fall, and only eight when the winter was over.

Do you wonder, Guillaume, that, sad and half-sick as we were, we were joyful when the snow melted and we saw the first bit of brown earth? It was only a wee bit, not half so large as your little garden, but it meant that the horrible cold had almost gone. Monster icicles rattled down from the Rock. The sky was not so gray and gloomy. The days were growing longer. The bit of brown earth became larger, and the sunshine was warmer.

By and by the winter was over, the summer had come, the ice had long ago gone from the river. Every morning someone would say, "Maybe there will be news of a ship today." At night we were sure to hear, "She did not come today, but she is one day nearer than she was yesterday."

At last, one bright June morning, we caught sight of a little white sail not far distant. It brought us a joyful message. Think how happy we were when we heard that Captain Pontgravé was at Tadousac! We almost felt as if we were on our way home, for now we should learn what had been going on in France and we should hear from our friends. You can guess what I said to myself, little brother. It was, "Now I shall hear from Guillaume!" I kept saying this over and over in my mind as I went down to the boat with the Governor.

In a little more than two days we were at Tadousac. There was the ship. There was the captain with his men. Best of all, there was a long, long letter from Nurse that told me all about you, that you were well and good, and that you did not forget, far away over the sea,

Your big brother,

HENRI

Eva March Tappan

FRENCH PIONEERS

NEW FRANCE, New Spain, New England,
Which will it be?
Who will win the new land,
The land across the sea?

They came here, they toiled here,
They broke their hearts afar,
Normandy and Brittany,
Paris and Navarre.

They lost here, at last here;
It wasn't so to be.
Let us still remember them,
Men from oversea.

Marquette and Joliet,
Cartier, La Salle,
Priest, corsair, gentleman,
Gallants, one and all.

France was in their quick words,
France was in their veins.
They came here, they toiled here;
They suffered many pains.

Lake and river, stream and wood,
Seigneurs and dames —
They lived here, they died here,
They left singing names.

Rosemary and *Stephen Vincent Benét*

383

DANIEL BOONE was fourteen and "nigh growed," according to his father, when the pair made a long trek from Pennsylvania down into the Carolinas. The Alleghenies through which they tramped were wild and unexplored and full of danger. Both French and English were trying to secure a hold on the region by making the Indians their allies. In 1749 this rivalry was leading directly to the French and Indian War which broke out a few years later.

In the woods Dan was separated from his father and was captured by a party of Iroquois Indians and French Canadians. These forest scouts, who were called "coureurs de bois," had come down under Captain Prideau to try to make an alliance with the Cherokee Indians before the English should succeed in winning the tribe over to their side.

For two nights following his capture, Dan had slept very little. With his hands bound behind him and fastened to the base of a tree, he could lie only on one side, with the roots pressing into his ribs. The chilly mountain air cut through his buckskin hunting shirt and leggings. His buckskin robe was still strapped to his back but he could not get at it. He lay cramped and shivering too far from the fire to receive any of its warmth.

Close to him was another prisoner, a grim, wiry little

man with a week-old beard the color of a carrot. His mouth made Dan think of a steel trap. On his head was a cap made from the skin of a black fox.

Once in a while they managed to exchange a whispered word. Dan learned that Jody Brent was a member of George Washington's surveying party which had gone out to make a map of this wilderness. Dan himself had met the young surveyor in the woods only a few days before.

When the third morning of the march began, even the hardy coureurs de bois were tired and grumbling, for Captain Prideau had driven them until late the night before. An Iroquois runner had reported that the English were nearing a pass to the south, and the news had sent Captain Prideau into a rage. The pass, so Jody Brent whispered to Dan, led across the great wall of the Alleghenies and was on the main route to the Cherokee towns. To succeed in his mission of buying the aid of the Cherokees in the approaching French and Indian War, Captain Prideau must reach the spot first with his bags and bundles of "bribe goods."

"Know what's in them bags, son?" whispered Jody Brent to Dan.

"I been wonderin' about it a heap," said Dan under his breath.

"In the bags, son, you'll find the price of a thousand lives. There's enough beads and wampum, enough mirrors and knives and ribbons and gewgaws to buy every English scalp from here to Virginia. And don't think the

Cherokees won't be bought by it. If these bribe goods ever reaches the big Indian council that's comin', the English settlers in this wilderness won't have a chance for their lives."

Dan swallowed. "We've got to do something!" he said.

Jody agreed. But how were they to do it?

The two prisoners were carefully watched by the Iroquois, especially by Panther Tail, the Indian who had captured Dan and whose cruelty caused him to be hated by both prisoners.

Long before daylight the company was on the move again. Captain Prideau's voice could be heard the length of the line, swearing in both English and French, and jabbering heatedly in the Iroquois dialect, while he urged everyone on to the limit of endurance. Early as it was,

he was dressed neatly as always. Under his hunting shirt
of cream buckskin was another shirt of clean white linen.
He wore blue army trousers and shiny black military
boots. Buckled round his waist was a sword with a silver
hilt. His mustache was neatly waxed and his graying hair
was tied in a queue with a small red ribbon.

As they marched, men and horses fought and clawed
their way over rocks and through the dense scrub growth
of the high country. They pulled and pushed and strained
and finally managed to get the animals and all the baggage
to the bald mountaintop. Dan was more dead than alive
when he crawled over the edge and threw himself down
to rest.

387

The sharp sweet air revived him. He rolled over and stared with widening eyes at the wilderness that lay ahead, a country that few white men had ever seen.

For a moment he forgot that he was a prisoner. The spell of the land was on him. Mountains seemed to stretch forever into the west. They rose above the clouds, black and purple and then smoky blue far away. Each one seemed higher than the last, soaring heavenward above rolling seas of clouds. The clouds parted beneath him for an instant, and Dan could see a river, winding like a silver ribbon through the valley below. Their route lay across that river, and southward.

Captain Prideau's sharp voice interrupted Dan's dreaming. The boy struggled painfully to his feet. As he did so, something small and sharp cut through the sole of his moccasin, lightly pricking his heel. It was a thin sliver of keen-edged flint.

His pulse gave a jump. Here was something that would cut the cords with which he was bound every night. No one noticed as his fingers closed quickly over the flint and slipped it into the pouch at his belt.

Slipping, sliding, hurrying every foot of the way, the company plunged downward toward the river. Captain Prideau's voice was never still for a minute. He wanted to be far beyond the next mountain hump before dark caught them.

Finally the men reached the bottom. They stumbled out through the trees and stood open-mouthed on the river bank. Captain Prideau's voice died. He stared at the water. For a while afterward there was silence. It was not a large stream, and normally it could have been waded without much trouble. But there was no chance of wading it today. It was a swirling muddy flood.

Captain Prideau's face grew purple. He shook his fists at the skies and at the river. He choked, got his breath, and all at once he was snapping orders.

Men threw aside their packs and seized axes. They attacked the pines and whatever light wood they could find. Others dragged the timbers down to the water's edge and began building a raft. No chance could be taken with the precious bribe goods. Every bag and bundle must be floated safely across. The men themselves could swim behind the raft and push it to the other side.

The raft took form slowly. It had to be large and strongly built to carry so much valuable freight. Saplings were sprung over the ends of the logs and lashed with vines to hold them securely. Ropes from the pack horses were used for mooring lines. It was nearly dark before the work was finished.

Little attention was paid to the prisoners during this time. Dan kept his eyes open, watching for a chance to slip away through the trees. But his enemy, Panther Tail, was always near, his bow ready. One move, Dan knew, was all the excuse Panther Tail wanted to send an arrow into his back.

Every added minute of delay brought a fresh outburst of temper from Captain Prideau. Though dark was near, the raft must be loaded, the baggage must be ferried to the other side. Captain Prideau was determined to see this task finished before he made camp.

But Captain Prideau reckoned without the night and the weather. Black dark caught them before the loading was done, and the men had to work by torchlight. Then, as the last bundle was lashed in place, the rain began to pour down steadily.

It would be folly to attempt the crossing now. Captain Prideau threw up his hands and called a halt.

The raft was moored carefully between two pines leaning over the water. A guard was set to watch it, and the men hurriedly erected rude shelters against the rain. Some scraps of venison were tossed to the prisoners, then they were tied back to back and left lying under a tree. If they were wet through and cold and thoroughly miserable, no one cared.

With Jody Brent's hands and feet bound tightly to his own, Dan could hardly move. By raising his head a little he could see part of the camp, dimly lighted by two small fires. Beyond the edge of the trees he could barely make out the dark shape of the raft.

His eyes fastened on the raft and its deadly freight. He forgot the rain. He forgot the chill and the aching weariness that was in him. He knew only that he would never again have such a chance as this. If he escaped at all, it must be tonight.

He nudged Jody Brent with his elbow. His whisper was muffled by the sound of the rain and the river.

"Jody, we've got to keep awake. We've got to — understand?"

The little man twisted his head around until his answering whisper was almost in Dan's ear. "I'm with you, lad. But how are we going to break these cords?"

"I'll get us loose. I found something I can cut the ropes with. Wait until all the fires go out."

"All right. Can you swim, lad?"

"Yes. Can you?"

"Yes."

"Fine. We'll have to crawl to the water and swim to each end of the raft to untie the ropes. 'Twould be better if we had knives to cut them with."

"Yes," the little man whispered. "But we can't go out of our way to steal one. We can't take the extra risk."

They waited. Just keeping awake and waiting was the hardest part. The rain and the chill did not help much. The weariness of long days and unending miles of marching lay heavy upon them. Dan felt he could have lain down in a puddle of ice-cold mud and gone instantly to sleep.

He studied the camp and tried to plan each move. Several men lay between him and the water. It would not be easy, crawling around them in the dark. But the guard at the raft worried him more than anything else. He could not see the fellow yet, but he knew he must be under one of the trees where the raft was moored.

A shadow moved on the river bank. Dan watched it. He saw the guard stand up, cast a swift glance about the camp, then glide silently toward the prisoners. Firelight caught the fellow's face and Dan's heart seemed to turn over and stop beating for an instant.

The guard was his enemy, Panther Tail.

The Indian bent over and examined their cords. For long minutes afterward he stood scowling down at them, till it seemed as if he must have guessed their plans. At last he grunted and went back to the raft.

A DESPERATE ATTEMPT

When the night was jet-black dark, with not even a spark to show their movements, Dan began twisting cautiously, trying to reach the small pouch fastened at his belt. For a horrid moment he was afraid he could never force his bound hands around far enough to touch the

392

pouch. Then he managed to get the flint out, only to drop it somewhere on the ground between Jody and himself. It took nearly half an hour of frantic searching before he found it. It was impossible to cut the cords on his own wrists with it, but by holding the flint tightly between thumb and forefinger, he was able to insert it in the lower cords about Jody Brent's hands.

The flint was almost as sharp as a piece of glass. He sawed carefully up and down with it, trying to control his haste. Several times he was sure he cut Jody's wrists, but the little man uttered no sound. Suddenly Jody's hands were free.

Dan's heart began to beat wildly. Jody began fumbling with the rest of the cords tying them both. Dampness had swelled the knots. The little man wasted several minutes trying to untie them in the dark. Finally he cut them with the flint.

Now that they were both free, it was hard to resist a wild impulse to get up and run. Dan forced himself to lie still while he got his bearings. He was on the side nearest the water, and it would be up to him to lead the way.

The rain, he realized, had almost stopped. The sound of it would no longer muffle their movements. With a prayer that Panther Tail might be asleep, he turned over on his stomach and began crawling toward the river.

He inched along, feeling out the ground ahead of him with his fingers and carefully picking twigs and small stones from his path. Jody Brent followed. They were as silent as a pair of cats stalking a robin. They passed the first sleeping figure and turned to slip between two others. The black night was growing gray, and dim forms were beginning to take shape. Was dawn so near?

One of the horses snorted. The man on Dan's left stirred and rolled over. Dan stopped dead.

The man raised up on one elbow, rubbed his eyes, and looked squarely into Dan's face. Dan lay motionless. The man mumbled sleepily. Finally he settled down and pulled his robe over his head.

Dan dared not move for a long time afterward.

It was much lighter now. With a sinking feeling inside of him, Dan realized the cause — the moon. The night had cleared and the moon had come up over the far ridge. A bright full moon! It shone down on the river, clearly lighting the raft and the figure of Panther Tail hunched against a tree.

Dan swallowed. Nothing worse could have happened. Then he felt Jody Brent's hand on his moccasins, and he began to crawl forward again.

As they crept past the last sleeping figure, something bright peeping out under the fellow's robe caught his attention. It was a knife. Dan's fingers moved toward it, touched it, drew it gently from its case. The man slept on. With a glance at Panther Tail, Dan crept straight for the river, the knife between his teeth.

They reached the river's edge twenty feet below the raft. Shadows of the trees hid them as they crawled into the icy water up to their necks. Dan shook violently and nearly dropped the knife. Then he saw the raft upstream. On the bank at the far end of it sat Panther Tail, his chin on his chest. Was the Indian asleep? Dan stared at him, eyes straining to catch the least movement.

Dan gripped the roots under the bank and drew himself along in the shadow. The cold water swirled about his neck, tugged at his feet. Far downstream he could hear the roar of rapids. At the edge of the shadow he stopped. He looked long at Panther Tail, then glanced back at Jody Brent.

Jody's hand touched his shoulder. The little man's whisper was hardly audible above the sound of the river.

"Easy! Don't climb on the raft till we get it loose. I'll cut the front line. When she swings out in the current, you cut the back line quick."

It sounded easy enough. They kicked forward silently. A minute later they were safely across the stretch of moonlit water, and Jody Brent had vanished around the corner of the raft. Dan clung to the log where the rear line was tied, his knife ready to slash it the moment he felt the current swinging them clear.

Minutes passed. Dan realized that Jody must be having a struggle with the knots, which would be swelled tight in the water. Maybe he'd better cut the back line first and then swim around and give Jody the knife.

He raised his head cautiously for a look at Panther Tail. Sick fear shot through him. Panther Tail was awake and on his feet, and even now was moving along the bank to examine the moorings.

Dan gulped air and sank out of sight behind the corner log. It was hard to keep his body down. The current tore at his legs and swung him away from the raft, up toward the surface again. In desperation he pulled himself far under the logs.

He held this position until his lungs felt near to bursting. When he had stood the strain for the last possible second, he drew himself to the far side of the raft and thrust his face quickly to the surface.

He was gasping in the chill air when he saw Panther Tail crawling around the bags on the raft, almost directly above him. For one terrible fraction of a second Dan was sure the Indian had seen him. But Panther Tail was only looking after the lashings. Dan drew himself under again.

Where was Jody? The little man must be down here somewhere with him. Then he forgot about Jody in the

torture of holding his breath. It was suddenly more than he could bear. No matter what happened, he had to have air.

He fought his way to the side and thrust his nose to the surface. Finally he raised his head carefully and took a swift glance over the logs. Relief ran through him like a warm flood. Panther Tail was no longer on the raft.

Dan drew himself to the corner where the mooring line was fastened and studied the bank. Swiftly relief changed to uneasiness, and then to fright. Panther Tail was standing under a tree, peering back into the shadows under the trees where the men lay sleeping. He was peering at the spot where Jody and Dan had lately been tied.

Dan watched him. He saw Panther Tail take a step forward, stop, then suddenly fling his robe aside, and go running through the camp.

Dan waited no longer. He raised his knife and began hacking at the rope. His fingers were so numb that it was hard to grip the handle tight. Once the knife slipped and he nearly lost it.

"Quick, lad!" came Jody Brent's hoarse whisper. "Bring the knife here. I can't do anything with these knots!"

It was now or never. Dan grasped the handle with both hands, put his weight on it, and jerked the blade down over the rope. This time he cut through it.

Jody called again, urgently.

"Coming!" Dan gasped. He kicked madly, fighting against the current. He was so weak that it seemed as if he could never reach Jody in time. In a few seconds the whole camp would be aroused.

Jody's hand rose dripping in the moonlight and snatched the knife from him. The little man splashed for the upper mooring line. He reached it, and with a violent lunge he brought the knife down and cut through it with one stroke. Abruptly the raft was in motion.

It moved with painful slowness at first, drifting quietly a few feet from the bank. Then the current caught one end, spun it around, and swept it toward the middle of the stream, faster and faster. Dan hooked one leg over a log and tried to crawl aboard. He was too weak to pull himself up.

Back in camp a voice rose shrilly. Suddenly a man yelled, then another, and in the next instant the night rang with wild, angry voices.

398

Jody Brent succeeded in pulling himself over the corner. log. He lay there a moment, spent, then crawled slowly up on the raft.

"Hang on, lad!" he gasped, and began working around the edge of the baggage toward Dan. He caught Dan's hand, braced himself, and then drew Dan clear of the water.

Without a word they scrambled over the heap of baggage and began slashing and tearing at the coverings.

Flashes of musket fire stabbed the shadows behind them. Shots echoed over the water. Dan could hear cursing and angry shouting as men plunged through the underbrush and began running along the river bank. Captain Prideau was shrieking orders. Like a wolf pack in full cry, the French woodsmen and the Iroquois raced downstream to head off the raft.

The fury of those on shore was like the lash of a whip to the two on the raft. They worked madly. Jody Brent ripped open a bundle and a stream of glittering trade knives spilled over the logs. Dan seized one and hacked at the other bundles.

They slashed everything open and heaved the contents into the water. Bags of beads, mirrors, silks, steel heads for tomahawks — more beads and mirrors, spoons and silver bangles — belts and cups and kettles and a great bag of wampum. These would have been glittering wealth for a thousand painted warriors. As they opened the bundles, they kicked and shoved and spilled the contents over the side, and fed everything to the river.

Arrows hissed overhead. French and Indians leaped into the water and began swimming clumsily toward them. But they were too late.

Jody Brent kicked the last bundle away. "There go your bribe goods!" he yelled. He swung a huge belt of wampum above his head. "There goes your treaty!" He ripped the belt to shreds and flung it at the struggling swimmers.

He swayed from weariness and fell down beside Dan. The current was swiftly carrying the raft beyond pursuit. They had set out to accomplish the impossible, and they had done it.

Alexander Key

THE BUFFALO HUNT

AT last the day came when my father allowed me to go on a buffalo hunt with him. What a proud boy I was!

Ever since I could remember, my father had been teaching me the things that I should know and preparing me to be a good hunter. I had learned to make bows and to string them, and to make arrows and tip them with feathers. I was only eight years old, but I knew how to ride my pony no matter how fast he would go, and I felt that I was brave and did not fear danger. All these things I had learned for just this day when my father would allow me to go with him on a buffalo hunt.

This was the event for which every Sioux boy eagerly waited. The only other event which could equal it would be the day I went for the first time on the warpath to meet the enemy and protect my tribe.

Always, the evening before a buffalo hunt, an old man went around the circle of tepees calling, "I-ni-la, I-ni-la," not loudly, but so everyone could hear. The old man was saying, "Keep quiet. Keep quiet." We all knew that this meant that the scouts had come in and reported buffaloes near. It was not necessary to explain that tomorrow there would be a big hunt. The one word, "I-ni-la," was sufficient to bring quiet to the whole camp. That night there would be no calling or shouting from tepee to tepee and no child would cry aloud. Even the horses and dogs obeyed the command for quiet, and all night not a horse neighed and not a dog barked.

Such is the orderliness of a Sioux camp that men, women, children, and animals seem to have a common understanding and sympathy. It is no mystery, but natural, that the Indian and his animals should understand each other both with words and without words. There are words, however, that the Indian uses that are understood by both his horses and dogs. When on a hunt, if one of the warriors speaks the word "A-a-ah" rather quickly and sharply, every man, horse, and dog will stop instantly and listen. Not a move will be made by an animal until the men move or speak further. As long as the hunters listen, the animals will listen also.

It was in the fall of the year and the evening was cool as my father and I sat by the fire and talked over the coming hunt. I knew that my father did not expect me to get a buffalo at all, but only to try perhaps for a small calf should I be able to get close enough to one. Nevertheless, I was greatly excited as I sat and watched him working in his easy, firm way.

I was wearing my buffalo-skin robe, the hair next to my body. Mother had made me a rawhide belt and this, wrapped around my waist, held my blanket on when I threw it off my shoulders. In the early morning I would wear the blanket, for it would be cold. When it came time to shoot, I should not want it, but the belt would hold it in place.

You can picture me, I think, as I sat in the glow of the

campfire, my little brown body bare to the waist, watching, and listening intently to my father. My hair hung down my back and I wore moccasins and breech cloth of buckskin. To my belt was fastened a rawhide holster for my knife, for when I was eight years of age we had plenty of knives. I was proud to own one, and this night I remember I kept it on all night. Neither did I lay aside my bow, but went to sleep with it in my hand, thinking, I suppose, to be all the nearer ready in the morning when the start was made.

Father sharpened my steel points for me and also sharpened my knife. The whetstone was a long stone which was kept in a buckskin bag. Sometimes this stone went all over the camp; every tepee did not have one. I had, as I remember, about ten arrows. When my father was through sharpening them, I put them in my rawhide quiver. I had a rawhide quirt, too, which I would wear fastened to my waist. By the time all preparations had been made, Father had told me just how I was to act when I started out in the morning with the hunters. I paid careful attention to everything he said.

The next morning the hunters were catching their horses about daybreak. I arose with my father and went out and caught my pony. We brought our animals to the tepee and got our bows and arrows and mounted. From all over the village came the hunters. Most of them were leading their horses. These horses were anxious for the hunt and came prancing, their ears straight up and their tails waving in the air. We were soon joined by perhaps a hundred or more riders, some of whom carried bows and arrows and some of whom were armed with guns.

The buffaloes were reported to be about five or six miles away as we should count distance now. At that time we did not measure distance in miles. One "camping distance" was about ten miles, and these buffaloes were said to be about one half camping distance away.

My pony was a black one and a good runner. I felt very important as I rode along with the hunters and my father, the chief. I kept as close to him as I could.

Two men had been chosen to lead the party. These two men were, in a sense, policemen whose work it was to keep order. They carried large sticks of ash wood, something like a policeman's billy, though longer. The leaders rode ahead until they sighted the herd. Then they stopped and waited for the rest of us to ride up.

We all rode slowly toward the herd, which, on sight of us, had come together, although they had been scattered here and there over the plain. When they saw us, they all ran close together as if at the command of a leader. We continued riding slowly toward the herd until one of the leaders shouted, "Ho-ka-he!" which means, "Ready, go!" At that command every man started for the herd.

I had been listening, too, and the minute the hunters started, I started also. Away I went, my little pony putting all the speed he had into the race. It was not long before I lost sight of my father, but I kept going just the same. I threw my blanket back and the chill of the autumn morning struck my body, but I did not mind. On I went. It was wonderful to race over the ground with all these horsemen about me. There was no shouting, no noise of any kind except the pounding of the horses' feet. The herd was now running and had raised a cloud of dust.

I felt no fear until we had entered this cloud of dust and I could see nothing about me — only hear the sound of feet. Where was Father? Where was I going? On I rode through the cloud, for I knew I must keep going.

All at once, I realized that I was in the midst of the buffaloes, their dark bodies rushing all about me and their great heads moving up and down to the sound of their hoofs beating upon the earth. I leaned close down upon my little pony's body and clutched him tightly. I can never tell you how I felt toward my pony at that moment. All thought of shooting had left my mind. I was seized by blank fear.

In a moment or so, however, my senses became clearer, and I could distinguish other sounds besides the clatter of feet. I could hear a shot now and then and I could see the buffaloes beginning to break up into small bunches. I could not see my father or any of my companions yet, but my fear was vanishing and I was safe.

I let my pony run. The buffaloes looked too large for me to tackle anyway, so I just kept going. The herd became more and more scattered. Pretty soon I saw a young calf that looked about my size. I remembered then what my father had told me the night before as we sat about the fire. Those instructions were important now for me to follow.

I was still back of the calf, but trying to get alongside

406

him. I was anxious to get a shot, yet afraid to try, as I was still very nervous. While my pony was making all speed to come alongside, I chanced a shot and to my surprise my arrow landed. My second arrow glanced along the back of the animal and sped on between the horns, making only a slight wound. My third arrow hit a spot that made the running beast slow up in his gait. I shot a fourth arrow, and though it, too, landed, it was not a fatal wound.

It seemed to me that it was taking a lot of shots, and I was not proud of my marksmanship. I was glad, however, to see the animal going slower and I knew that one more shot would make me a hunter.

My horse seemed to know his own importance. His

two ears stood straight forward and it was not necessary for me to urge him to get closer to the buffalo. I was soon by the side of the buffalo, and one more shot brought the chase to a close.

I jumped from my pony. As I stood by my fallen game, I looked all around, wishing that the world could see. But I was alone. In my determination to stay by until I had won my buffalo, I had not noticed that I was far from everyone else. No admiring friends were about. As far as I could see, I was alone on the plain. The herd of buffaloes had completely disappeared. As for my father, much as I wished for him, I had no idea where he was.

I stood and looked at the animal on the ground. I was happy. Everyone must know that I, Ota K'te, had killed a buffalo. I must then take something from this animal to show that I had killed it. I took all the arrows, one by one, from the body. As I took them out, it occurred to me that I had used five arrows. If I had been a skillful hunter, one would have been sufficient.

Here it was that temptation came to me. Why could I not take out two of the arrows and throw them away? No one would know, and then I should be more greatly admired and praised as a hunter. As it was, I knew that I should be praised by Father and Mother, but I wanted more. And so I was tempted to lie.

I was planning this as I took out my skinning knife that Father had sharpened for me the night before. I skinned one side of the animal, but when it came to turning the buffalo over, I was too small.

408

I was wondering what to do when I heard my father's voice calling, "To-ki-i-la-la-hu-wo." "Where are you?"

I quickly jumped on my pony and rode to the top of a little hill near by. Father saw me and came to me at once. He was pleased to see me and to know that I was safe. I knew then that I could never lie to my father. He was too fond of me and I too proud of him. He had always told me to tell the truth. He wanted me to be an honest man. I resolved then to tell the truth even if it took from me a a little glory.

He rode up to me with a glad expression on his face, expecting me to go back with him to his kill. As he came up, I said as calmly as I could, "Father, I have killed a buffalo." His smile changed to surprise and he asked me where my buffalo was. I pointed to it and we rode over to where it lay, partly skinned.

Father set to work to skin it for me. I had watched him do this many times and knew perfectly well how to do it myself, but I could not turn the animal over. Father did this for me, while I helped all I could. When the hide was off, he put it on the pony's back with the hair side next to the pony. On this he arranged the meat so that it would balance. Then he covered the meat carefully with the rest of the hide, so that no dust would reach it while we traveled home.

I rode home on top of the load. I showed my father the arrows that I had used and just where the animal had been hit. He was very much pleased and praised me over and over again. I felt more glad than ever that I had told

409

the truth. I have never regretted it. I am more proud now that I told the truth than I am of killing the buffalo.

We then rode to where my father had killed a buffalo. There we stopped and prepared it for taking home.

It was late afternoon when we got back to camp. No king who rode in state was ever more proud than I that day as I came into the village sitting high up on my load of buffalo meat.

It is not customary for Indian men to brag about their exploits and I had been taught that bragging was not manly. So I was very quiet, although I was bursting with pride. Always on arriving home I would run out to play with the other boys, but this day I lingered close to the tepee so that I could hear the nice things that were said about me. It was soon all over camp that Ota K'te had killed a buffalo.

My father was so proud that he gave away a fine horse. He called an old man to our tepee to cry out the news to the rest of the people in camp. The old man stood outside the door and sang a song of praise to my father. I stood holding the horse by a rope. The man who was doing the singing called another old man, who was to receive the horse as a present. He accepted the horse by coming up to me, holding out his hands to me, and saying, "Ha-ye," which means "Thank you." The old man went away very grateful for the horse.

That ended my first and last buffalo hunt. It lives only in my memory, for the days of the buffalo are over.

Chief Luther Standing Bear

CODY'S BOY

Cody's boy or, as his mother called him, Willie, was sitting on the porch of the double log house at Salt Valley Creek in Kansas, wondering what to do next. His father was dead. He had left behind, besides Will, five girls and a delicate, though fearless, wife, now fighting an unjust claim on her home. Will, eleven years old and the eldest, must take his father's place.

Suddenly he rose and went into the house.

"Mother," he said, touching her shoulder, "I've thought of a way to make some money for you. If you'll go with me to Leavenworth, I'll ask Mr. Major, of Russell, Waddell, and Major, for a job as an extra on one of their wagon trains. They know me now. I've herded cattle for them. They pay good money and I can help you settle this lawsuit."

His mother's eyes looked anxiously into his. "You're too young for such hard work, son," she protested.

"But, Mother, I'm a good rider and a good shot."

"Yes, I know," she sighed, pondering over his words. "I suppose, as things are, you must try it."

No longer could Will Cody act the mischievous, teasing brother who scalped his sisters' dolls, or the rascal who chased away the best, yellow-skinned chickens when the minister was coming to dinner. He must be a man at eleven years old.

Next day, with a look of determination in his eyes, Will Cody signed a pledge in a contractor's office at Leavenworth, Kansas. His mother stood beside him. The pledge ran:

"I, William F. Cody, do hereby solemnly swear before the great and living God, that during my engagement with and while I am in the employ of Russell, Waddell, and Major, I will under no circumstances use profane language, that I will not quarrel or fight with any other employee of the firm, and that in every respect I will conduct myself honestly, be faithful to my duties, and so direct all my acts as to win the confidence of my employers. So help me, God!"

Will finished the scribbled signature. Already his fingers were stiff from holding the pen, for he had had but little schooling.

Mr. Major had decided to test him for one trip.

"You can try it, boy," he had said, kindly. "I know you're a good shot — that's why I'm letting you go." Moreover, he felt sorry for the boy and sorrier yet for the widowed mother left alone with all those children and a lawsuit on her hands. The trip would last but sixty days and he hoped Will would come through safely.

The train Will was to join in this May of 1857 was going to Salt Lake City with a herd of beef cattle for General Albert S. Johnston's army. The canvas-topped wagons were hauled by oxen. A tender, known as a "bull whacker," was told off to each wagon to keep the slow oxen going at a fairly steady rate. Thus a pace was maintained for the entire train — thirty-five wagons in all. Will Cody was assigned to his special wagon. In addition, since he was the youngest in the party, he was selected to ride up and down the train delivering necessary messages. He was all enthusiasm for his job, though he found it hard at times to keep up his high spirits.

"Those pesky oxen would never make it if you gave them all the time left in the world," he muttered to himself. But his interest did not flag and camping out at night was his great joy. The great shadowy prairie, the canopy of stars overhead, the blazing, roaring fires, and the good meal cooking in the mess kettles were all equally delightful.

Yet at the back of Will's mind and everyone else's mind lurked the thought of Indians. When and where would they attack? Nobody ever heard of a big wagon train crossing the plains without a surprise encounter.

413

Will made the most of his first happy days, but later days were to come when the work he had so bravely undertaken seemed tiresome indeed and the men shouted, "Get along there now, Billy! Stir your stumps! This trip's no Sunday picnic!" On those occasions he was often a weary boy, but he did not grumble or complain.

INDIAN RAIDERS

Thirty-odd miles west of Fort Kearney was Plum Creek, the stream that fed the South Platte River. Here, at noon one day, after a long drive the train camped, posting several guards. While a number of the drivers napped under the mess wagons, the boy driver, Will, watched with deepest interest the preparation of the stew for dinner. Suddenly arrows flew from the thicket a few hundred yards away. Wild yells accompanied them.

As war whoops, "Ai-ai-ah-ai," made the air ring, Indian warriors charged the camp at a swift gallop. Down went the three guards. The other men, seizing their guns, lined up behind the wagons. From this bulwark they poured a shower of bullets upon the enemy. After shooting one man through the leg, the Indians fell back, disappearing as quickly as they had come. But the experienced heads of the wagon train, Frank and Bill McCarthy, knew well enough that this withdrawal was only temporary.

"What are we going to do?" whispered Will coolly to the wagon master.

"Good for you, Billy! You didn't scare worth a cent,"

answered Frank proudly. "We've got to make Fort Kearney by way of the creek and the river. Those Indians have got us just where they want us. We'll have to leave the beasts and wagons and run for the creek. Then we can use the bank for a breastwork!"

Oxen and wagons must, of necessity, be left behind. The Indians worried the men continually. Guns kept the

Indians at bay until the party reached a place where the creek made a junction with the Platte River. Here the wounded man could no longer wade, though steadied by a stronger comrade who kept an arm round his shoulders. Since many others could not swim, the party halted until a raft of poles could be made. On this the helpless man was finally borne along, swimmers pushing him. The raft was also used for carrying their heavy rifles.

Young Will cared little that there could be no halts, no time taken off to cook a meal, only hours of steady plodding through the water. He was happy over the praise given him by the wagon master. He scorned the help of the raft when McCarthy said, "Now, Billy, if you want a rest, mount the raft and we'll carry you!"

"Let the sick be carried," said Cody's boy. He knew how to swim.

Actually, by the time night came, he felt quite sick from fatigue but he did not say so. His buckskin clothes and heavy coonskin cap were waterlogged, the cap having fallen into the river several times. His boots felt like lead.

That night the moon, as if to punish still further the train of straggling men, was full and bright. Its light exposed them utterly to the Indians who were following closely, watching every chance for attack.

Now the boy driver lagged yards behind the others in the shadow of the river bank that was his only protection. He was so tired that he seemed to be walking in his sleep. What was that? A gorgeous red flower nodding like a plume over the bank ahead of him? It leaned over still

416

more and then it moved! For an instant Will stared, frozen in his tracks. What he thought was a flower was really the bright red headdress of an Indian! Its owner was peering farther and farther over the bank, prepared to take aim at Will with an arrow.

Should he fire? Yes, and without hesitation. Will had to choose between killing the Indian and sacrificing one of his friends. Bang went the gun! Crash! To his amazement, the tall body of a dead Indian tumbled into the river at his feet.

Frank McCarthy heard Will's shot. He was responsible for this crazy youngster. Rushing back to look for Will, he saw the boy pull an Indian's body out of the water.

"Blazes, if little Billy's not killed his man! Is that your first Indian, boy?"

Will nodded, feeling no pride in the achievement. This did not seem a great deed, but horrible, even though done in self-defense.

"Shall we bury him?" Will asked McCarthy.

"Bury him? I guess not. There's plenty more where he came from. Follow me close now. We've got to get along."

Fort Kearney was reached with the dawn, just as the bugle sounded reveille, but there was nothing triumphant about the party's entry. The train had been wrecked, the wagons and their contents burned by the Indians. The cattle had stampeded to join the buffaloes, and the men from Leavenworth were lucky to have escaped with their lives.

When they reached home in July, Will, to his great dismay, was interviewed by a reporter and saw his name in print with the title, "Boy Indian Slayer." He did not like this public attention. Still, he had been in actual combat with the enemy and had escaped. He was thankful, too, to put in his mother's lap what little money he had earned on this first adventure.

A DESPERATE STAND

The following summer, Will Cody was off again on another trip. This time the wagon train was to carry supplies to General Johnston's army at Fort Bridger. The route was known to be a dangerous one and plenty of teams and men were needed. Though the pay was forty dollars a month in gold, volunteers were hard to find. Lew Simpson, an old and seasoned wagon master, was to start with ten wagons direct for Salt Lake City. He asked Will if he would like to go as an extra hand and promised that his duties should not be heavy. If one of the drivers was sick or laid off, the boy was to take his place.

"I'll go," was the eager answer.

"You shall have your own mule, Billy, and only take orders from me," was the promise that clinched the matter.

The wagons used by Russell, Waddell, and Major were made especially for them and extra strong. They could carry six or seven thousand pounds of freight each, and their interiors were as large as the rooms of an ordinary-

418

sized house. The covers, made of two enormous canvas sheets each, kept out the rain.

A train, often called a "bull outfit," was made up of twenty-five wagons. A wagon master was put in charge of them. He had an assistant who was second in command. The thirty-five men in the train were divided into messes of seven apiece. All were heavily armed, carrying Colt pistols and Mississippi rifles.

At first sight, the outfit would have seemed a difficult one to surprise. But once again the men who led it were unfortunate when they reached the South Platte River. Here they fell in with a group of hostile settlers, who robbed them of all their freight and supplies. Only one of all the wagons was allowed to go on its way. When young Will and the others reached Fort Bridger, they received bad news. Two other supply trains had been captured and burned in the same manner. Consequently, at the Fort (where they now had to spend the winter), all were put on one-quarter rations and nearly starved before the spring came. Their fuel, too, had to be carried on their backs or on sleds, for the mules and oxen were killed for food. Poor Will, as well as his mates, had a season of thorough toughening.

At last, one happy spring day, he rejoiced at mounting a mule again and galloping away over the plains. Every day he drew nearer to the meeting with his mother and sisters. On leaving Fort Bridger for the Missouri River, the party had made a halt at another fort, Laramie. Here they met a supply train bound westward with plenty of food. All the hungry men feasted on coffee, hardtack, beans, and bacon, and Will, for once, had to let out his belt instead of tightening it.

Simpson and the others decided to accompany this train with its four hundred extra men to Leavenworth and home. They made Simpson wagon master and put him in charge of the two wagon trains, which were to travel fifteen to twenty miles apart. By this arrangement both trains could not be surprised and attacked at the same instant.

Swinging along on his mule, Cody's boy was light-hearted. Beside him rode Simpson himself and a man named Woods. The three had left the rear train early that day to go on a tour of inspection to the forward one. Seven miles had been covered.

They were on flat ground back of Cedar Bluffs when Simpson said good-naturedly, "Billy, that's a right good beast you got there." At the same moment, the boy saw Simpson change color. His keen eyes had spied a band of Indians coming out of a ravine half a mile away.

"Boys," he muttered, "we're in for it. Jump off and kill your mules. We'll use them for a barricade. Billy, you're a dead shot. See that Indian in the lead? To judge by his headdress, he's the chief. You get him."

Will, who loved animals, was quite dazed. "Must we kill the mules?" he asked, reluctantly.

"Yes, and there's no time to lose. Do what I say."

Simpson was already on the ground. A crack of his rifle made his mule tumble limply to earth. The other two speedily followed and the mules were dragged into a sort of bulwark just as the wheeling Indians surrounded them. Arrows flew like mad, but bullets were more effective. With a fearful yell the chief dropped, shot through the heart. His braves galloped away for a few minutes but soon returned.

Will Cody, as well as his seniors, now realized that they were in deadly danger. They were caught between the two wagon trains and without any hope of rescue that night. Their only advantage was their rifle fire, until powder and shot should give out. Then revolvers would be the weapon; next, at close fighting, knives; and then — nothing! Only three scalped bodies would mark the spot where they had been taken unawares. Already the Indians, cunningly hanging on the far side of their ponies, where they could not be reached, were sending forth a volley of arrows.

When the Indians drew off again to plot another attack, the three comrades worked on their barricade. Piling more and more loose dirt on the mules' bodies, they made it higher. They did not dare let themselves think of the lonely night hours now drawing on.

"Look, Billy!" Woods, the third man, who had been wounded in the shoulder, was pointing to a curtain of living fire, slowly but surely moving and dancing in their direction. The Indians had cleverly set the prairie grass ablaze. Coughing and half smothered in the dense smoke, the three still held out. Their screen of mule flesh and sod prevented the flames from reaching them.

All at once, the Indians seemed to decide that they would abandon the attack for the night. They drew off into the twilight. Will, though only twelve, guessed what their plan was. They would make a surprise attack later on in the dark.

Simpson and Will agreed that Woods, who had lost a great deal of blood, must be allowed to sleep. The others would spell each other through the night hours.

Will took the first watch. Not a sign, not a movement stirred the silent prairie, but he stayed wide awake. One never knew where Indians were nor what they might be up to. When Simpson relieved him, Will dropped asleep like a shot and dreamed a wild dream.

In the dream his dog, Turk, the mastiff at home, came to him, barking furiously, as if in warning. He opened his eyes with a start. What was wrong? Something, yes, was decidedly wrong. Simpson, who was supposed to be on guard, lay soundly sleeping and snoring. Will's eyes, the eyes of a natural scout, saw that forms were creeping, creeping up on them in the dark. He shook Simpson silently. Simpson roused Woods. A fresh blaze of fire from all three rifles cleared the trail. But their situation seemed hopeless. Day was breaking in the sky and they were now in plain view again.

If help would only come from their second wagon train! Where was it? Could it reach them in time? Weary hours dragged on. The Indians kept watch on their victims, who were outnumbered, ten to one.

Suddenly, Will and the two men saw that the Indians were talking among themselves and beginning to mount their ponies. What was alarming them? Simpson laid his ear to the earth. Yes, the Indians had heard what Will and his friends had failed to hear — the sound of animals' hoofs, the cracking whips of the men who walked beside them. Oh, sweet, sweet sound! Soon the men came in sight, rushing to their comrades' rescue. The Indians had already fled with a final shower of arrows.

The desperate stand behind the dead mules was over. Will felt his head to see if his hair was still on tight. Now the rescuers crowded round the three men. They slapped Will on the back, cheering and praising him.

He did not know that he was starting on his long career of Indian fighter, army scout, and Wild West showman, which would make his nickname of "Buffalo Bill" known the world over.

Laura Benét

GLOSSARY

The glossary gives 373 selected words appearing in this book. The meaning of each word is explained in a definition which fits the way it is used here. The page numbers show where each word may be found with the meaning given. In this glossary, as in a dictionary, there are guide words at the top of each page. The word at the left top is the first word listed on that page, and the word at the right top is the last word listed on the same page. Each word in the list is first divided into syllables and the accent is marked. Then the pronunciation is given in parentheses after each word. Little marks are used with some of the letters in the pronunciation of a word. These marks tell the sounds those letters have in the word. The list below and the words at the bottom of the right-hand pages show which sound of a letter each pronunciation mark means.

ā	as in dāte	ē	as in bē	ō	as in hōpe
ă	as in ăm	ĕ	as in mĕt	ŏ	as in hŏt
â	as in fâre	ę	as in hęre	ô	as in lôrd
ȧ	as in ȧsk	ẽ	as in makẽr	ū	as in ūse
ạ	as in ạbout	ī	as in bīte	ŭ	as in ŭp
ä	as in fär	ĭ	as in bĭt	û	as in bûrn

th	as in thin	ōō	as in fōōd
th	as in then	ŏŏ	as in fŏŏt
tū	as in pictūre	ou	as in out

A

ab sorbed' (ăb sôrbd'), greatly interested. (p. 363)

a chieve'ment (ạ chēv'mĕnt), something accomplished with courage or effort. (p. 417)

ad ven'ture some (ăd vĕn'tūrsŭm), daring; fond of adventures. (p. 84)

a gog' (ạ gŏg'), eager. (p. 346)

a ground' (ạ ground'), on the shore; on the bottom in shallow water. (p. 18)

a lee' (ạ lē'), toward the sheltered side. (p. 125)

al li'ance (ă lī'ăns), a union formed by an agreement. (p. 384)

a mid'ships (ạ mĭd'shĭps), in the middle of a ship. (p. 19)

424

an tic i pa'tion (ăn tĭs ĭ pā'shŭn), a looking forward to. (p. 102)

anx i'e ty (ăng zī'ĕ tĭ), fear about what may happen; worry. (p. 58)

ap pren'tice (ă prĕn'tĭs), a person who is learning a trade by working at it. (p. 255)

art'ful (ärt'fo͝ol), deceitful. (p. 358)

as sur'ance (ă sho͝or'ăns), an air of certainty. (p. 188)

at'mos phere (ăt'mŏs fẹr), air, feeling. (p. 253)

au'di ble (ô'dĭ b'l), loud enough to be heard. (p. 395)

a wry' (ạ rī'), wrong; out of order. (p. 72)

B

back'woods (băk'wo͝odz), forest regions far away from towns. (p. 215)

ban'gles (băng'g'lz), rings worn around the wrist, arm, or ankle. (p. 399)

bar ri cade' (băr ĭ kād'), a hastily made barrier for defense. (p. 420)

bay'ber ry (bā'bĕr ĭ), a shrub having a waxy berry, common on the seacoast. (p. 281)

bay'-col ored (bā'kŭl ērd), reddish brown. (p. 50)

be drag'gled (bē drăg'ld), much soiled. (p. 361)

bell'-cast er (bĕl'càs tēr), a man who makes bells. (p. 248)

blanched (blȧnchd), made white; pale. (p. 213)

bland (blănd), mild. (p. 334)

bleak (blēk), dreary. (p. 15)

blus'ter (blŭs'tēr), noisy talk. (p. 326)

Bo go ta' (bō gō tä'), the capital of Colombia. (p. 298)

bo le a do'ras (bō lä ä tho͞'räs), a lasso of leather or rope, having balls on the ends. (p. 55)

bram'bles (brăm'b'lz), shrubs covered with little thorns that prick. (p. 200)

breast'work (brĕst'wûrk), a low, hastily built wall for defense. (p. 415)

breech' cloth (brēch' clŏth), a cloth worn about the middle of the body. (p. 403)

bris'tling (brĭs'lĭng), coarse; rough. (p. 48)

broad'side (brôd'sīd), against the side. (p. 87)

bro cad'ed (brō kād'ĕd), made of stiff, expensive cloth with raised designs on it. (p. 164)

bro'ker (brō'kēr), an agent. (p. 180)

buck (bŭk), male deer. (p. 367)

dāte, ăm, fâre, àsk, ạbout, fär, bē, mĕt, hẹre, makēr, bīte, bĭt, hōpe, hŏt, lôrd, ūse, ŭp, bûrn, thin, then, pictụre, fo͞od, fo͝ot, out

425

bul'wark (bŏol'wêrk), a wall of defense. (p. 414)

bump'er (bŭmp'ẽr), unusually large. (p. 145)

bunk'house (bŭngk'hous), a rough building having simple sleeping quarters. (p. 337)

bur'row (bûr'ō), a hole dug in the ground. (p. 37)

bus'tling (bŭs'lĭng), in a hurry and making a noise. (p. 11)

by'-prod uct (bī'prŏd ŭkt), a thing produced in making another thing. (p. 152)

C

cal'drons (kôl'drŭnz), large kettles or boilers. (p. 146)

can'o py (kăn'ō pĭ), a roof-like covering. (p. 413)

can'ter (kăn'tẽr), to gallop gently. (p. 55)

ca'pered (kā'pẽrd), romped; jumped playfully. (p. 118)

cap sized' (kăp sīzd'), overturned. (p. 16)

Car ib be'an (kăr ĭ bē'ăn), the sea between the West Indies and Central America. (p. 292)

Car tier', Jacques (kàr tyā', zhàk), a French explorer. (p. 383)

car'tridge (kär'trĭj), a small tube made of metal or cardboard and containing a bullet and gunpowder. (p. 319)

426

cat'a ract (kăt'ạ răkt), a large, steep waterfall. (p. 365)

cat'boat (kăt'bōt), a sailboat having a single mast. (p. 127)

cav a liers' (kăv ạ lẽrz'), military men of noble rank. (p. 295)

ca vort' (kạ vôrt'), to caper or frolic. (p. 323)

Cham plain', Sieur de (shăm plān', syûr dẽ), a French explorer. (p. 369)

cher'ished (chẽr'ĭshd), held dear. (p. 238)

Cher o kees' (chẽr ō kēz'), one of the Iroquois tribes. (p. 386)

chron'i clers (krŏn'ĭ klẽrz), historians. (p. 297)

chuck wag'on (chŭk wăg'ŭn), a wagon carrying a stove and provisions for cooking, as in a lumber camp. (p. 119)

cinch (sĭnch), a strong band that holds a saddle in place. (p. 50)

Chim bo ra'zo (chĭm bō rä'zō), a mountain in Ecuador, South America. (p. 27)

clam'ber (klăm'bẽr), to climb, using hands and feet. (p. 296)

cleat (klēt), a piece of wood around which a sail rope is wound. (p. 135)

clenched (klĕnchd), closed tightly together. (p. 93)

clinched (klĭnchd), settled, decided. (p. 418)

com′ment (kŏm′ĕnt), a remark. (p. 172)

con′dor (kŏn′dēr), a large South American bird that eats the flesh of dead animals. (p. 23)

con′scious (kŏn′shŭs), realizing; aware. (p. 20)

con trac′tor (kŏn trăk′tēr), a person who agrees to do a piece of work under conditions agreed upon. (p. 412)

con veyed′ (kŏn vāyd′), carried. (p. 346)

cor′mo rants (kôr′mō răntz), large greedy birds with a long neck and a pouch under the beak. (p. 370)

cor′sair (kôr′sâr), a pirate. (p. 383)

coun′ty seat (koun′tĭ sēt), the town in which the county offices are located. (p. 324)

cou-reurs′ de bois′ (kōō rûr′dē bwȧ), forest scouts. (p. 384)

cox (kŏks), the person who steers a boat. (p. 106)

crack′lings (krăk′lĭngz), bits of pork fat fried crisp. (p. 302)

cred′it col′umn (krĕd′ĭt kŏl′ŭm), a column of figures showing how much a customer owes. (p. 325)

crev′ice (krĕv′ĭs), a gap or opening; a crack. (p. 27)

crit′i cal (krĭt′ĭ kăl), examining. (p. 147)

cro cheted′ (krō shād′), made of yarn or twine by hand. (p. 186)

cun′ning ly (kŭn′ĭng lĭ), cleverly. (p. 421)

cu′po la (kū′pō lȧ), a small dome on a roof. (p. 286)

cy′press es (sī′prĕs ĕz), evergreens. (p. 197)

D

dea′con (dē′kŭn), an officer of a church. (p. 220)

decked up (dĕkt ŭp), piled up on a platform. (p. 336)

del e ga′tion (dĕl ē gā′shŭn), a group acting for others. (p. 338)

del′uge (dĕl′ūj), a downpour. (p. 97)

de na′tured (dē nā′tūrd), made unfit for drinking. (p. 152)

de tain′ing (dē tān′ĭng), keeping back. (p. 142)

dex′trin (dĕks′trĭn), a sticky corn product. (p. 152)

di ag′o nal ly (dī ăg′ō năl ĭ), in a slanting direction. (p. 27)

di′a lect (dī′ȧ lĕkt), the form of speech used by a special class or group. (p. 386)

di am′e ter (dī ăm′ē tēr), the width of a circle. (p. 33)

---

dāte, ăm, fâre, ȧsk, ȧbout, fär, bē, mĕt, hēre, makēr, bīte, bĭt, hōpe, hŏt, lôrd, ūse, ŭp, bûrn, thin, then, pictūre, fōōd, fŏŏt, out

dis o blig'ing   (dĭs ō blīj'ĭng),
not helpful; refusing to do fa-
vors. (p. 358)

dog'ged (dŏg'ĕd), determined;
refusing to give up. (p. 18)

dou'ble hitch (dŭb"l hĭch), a
temporary but tight loop
around an object. (p. 55)

dove'cot (dŭv'kŏt), a house for
doves. (p. 374)

drib'bling (drĭb'lĭng), flowing
in small amounts. (p. 343)

duf'fel bag (dŭf'ĕl băg), a bag
of coarse woolen cloth, used
by sailors to carry belongings.
(p. 286)

Dutch ov'en (dŭch ŭv'ĕn), a
brick oven, in which food is
cooked by heated bricks after
the fire has died out. (p. 173)

E

Ec'ua dor (ĕk'wȧ dôr), a country in South America. (p. 23)

eels (ēlz), long, slippery fish that
look like snakes. (p. 376)

em'bers (ĕm'bērz), pieces of
wood or coals from a fire, still
burning a little. (p. 236)

e merged' (ē mûrjd'), came out.
(p. 70)

e mer'gen cy (ē mûr'jĕn sĭ), a
need for immediate action.
(p. 339)

en act'ed (ĕn ăkt'ĕd), per-
formed. (p. 346)

en coun'ter (ĕn koun'tēr), battle. (p. 413)

en dur'ance (ĕn dūr'ăns), power
to hold out. (p. 26)

en gi neer'ing (ĕn jĭ nēr'ĭng),
having to do with building
roads, bridges, etc. (p. 23)

en tan'gled (ĕn tăng'g'ld),
caught in a twisted and knotted mass of things. (p. 55)

ep'i sodes (ĕp'ĭ sōdz), sets of
events. (p. 347)

es teemed' (es tēmd'), respected;
thought well of. (p. 83)

ex haus'tion (ĕg zôs'chŭn),
great weariness. (p. 18)

ex hil'a rat ing (ĕg zil'ȧ rāt ĭng),
cheering; making lively. (p.
142)

ex panse' (ĕks păns'), an open
stretch. (p. 86)

ex'ploits (eks'ploitz), deeds of
daring. (p. 410)

F

fag'gots (făg'ŭtz), bundles of
twigs tied together for fuel.
(p. 230)

fal'ter (fôl'tēr), stumble; lose
courage. (p. 243)

fas'ci nat ed (făs'ĭ nāt ĕd),
charmed; with complete attention. (p. 24)

fath'om (făth'ŭm), the distance
six feet, used in measuring the
depth of water. (p. 22)

fiord (fyôrd), a long, narrow bay bordered by steep cliffs. (p. 61)

fit'ful (fĭt'fo͝ol), irregular. (p. 129)

flint'-lock (flĭnt' lŏk), an old-fashioned gun. (p. 15)

flour'ish (flûr'ĭsh), an extra ornament or curve. (p. 152)

foals (fōlz), colts; young horses. (p. 55)

fo''cas tle (fōk's'l), the forward part of a merchant ship, where the sailors live. (p. 81)

forge (fôrj), a place where iron or other metal is heated and beaten into shape. (p. 249)

fos'ter-moth er (fŏs'tẽr mŭth-ẽr), one who performs the duties of a mother. (p. 42)

fran'tic (frăn'tĭk), wild; violent. (p. 332)

fren'zied (frĕn'zĭd), excited; beyond control; mad. (p. 201)

friv'o lous (frĭv'ō lŭs), lacking sense; silly. (p. 247)

G

gal'lants (găl'ăntz), men noble in spirit. (p. 383)

gal'ley (găl'ĭ), the kitchen of a ship. (p. 274)

gam'bol ing (găm'bŭl ĭng), frolicking; playing. (p. 64)

gath'er ing way (găth'ẽr ĭng wā), beginning to move. (p. 284)

Gau'cho (gou'chō), a South American cowboy. (p. 48)

gaunt (gônt), bare. (p. 146)

gear (gẽr), equipment. (p. 367)

gew'gaws (gū'gôz), useless ornaments or toys. (p. 385)

ghast'ly (gȧst'lĭ), frightfully. (p. 212)

glu'ten (glo͞o'tĕn), the tough, sticky substance which remains in flour when the starch is taken out. (p. 152)

good'ly (go͝od'lĭ), fairly large; good-sized. (p. 330)

gor'y (gōr'ĭ), bloody. (p. 347)

gourd'ful (gōrd'fo͝ol), the amount held by a gourd hollowed out and used as a dipper or dish. (p. 255)

Gra na'da (grȧ nä'dȧ), province in southern Spain. (p. 290)

grange (grānj), an association of farmers. (p. 151)

grap'nel (grăp'nĕl), a small anchor with three or more hooks. (p. 22)

grat'i fied (grăt'ĭ fīd), pleased; satisfied. (p. 327)

green'backs (grēn'băks), bills; United States paper money printed in green. (p. 329)

---

dāte, ăm, fâre, ȧsk, ȧbout, fär, bē, mĕt, hẽre, makẽr, bīte, bĭt, hōpe, hŏt, lôrd, ūse, ŭp, bûrn, thin, then, pictῠre, fo͞od, fo͝ot, out

green'horn (grēn'hôrn), a person without experience. (p. 121)

green'ings (grēn'ĭngz), greenskinned apples. (p. 185)

grill (grĭl), a frame of bars with spaces between them. (p. 10)

grouse (grous), a food bird having feathered legs. (p. 357)

gua na'co (gwä nä'kō), a South American animal somewhat like a camel. (p. 49)

Guil laume' (gē yōm'), *William* in French. (p. 369)

gun'wale (gŭn'ĕl), the upper edge of a boat's side. (p. 20)

H

ham'per (hăm'pẽr), a large basket with a cover. (p. 3)

hard'tack (härd'tăk), a hard biscuit eaten by sailors. (p. 420)

haunts (hôntz), places often visited. (p. 368)

ha'ven (hā'vĕn), a place of shelter. (p. 62)

head'stones (hĕd'stōnz), name stones set up at the heads of graves. (p. 38)

head'wa ters (hĕd'wô tẽrz), the parts of a river near its source. (p. 336)

head'y (hĕd'ĭ), exhilarating; joy-bringing. (p. 142)

heat'ed ly (hēt'ĕd lĭ), violently; losing one's temper. (p. 386)

heir'loom (âr'lōōm), a possession handed down from generation to generation. (p. 245)

Hen ri' (ŏn rē'), *Henry* in French. (p. 381)

here by' (hẽr bī'), by this means. (p. 412)

hogs'head (hŏgz'hĕd), a large barrel. (p. 19)

hol'ster (hōl'stẽr), a leather case or holder. (p. 403)

hos'pi ta ble (hŏs'pĭ tạ b'l), welcoming. (p. 145)

hov'er ing (hŭv'ẽr ĭng), keeping near one place. (p. 315)

hue and cry (hū ănd crī), alarm; outcry. (p. 204)

hur'tle (hûr't'l), to rush violently. (p. 30)

I

im'pu dence (ĭm'pū dĕns), boldness and rudeness. (p. 326)

im pul'sive ly (ĭm pŭl'sĭv lĭ), acting suddenly, without thought beforehand. (p. 152)

in def'i nite ly (ĭn dĕf'ĭ nĭt lĭ), for an uncertain length of time. (p. 328)

in dif'fer ent (ĭn dĭf'ẽr ĕnt), not caring. (p. 234)

in fest'ed (ĭn fĕst'ĕd), overrun with. (p. 169)

in fir'ma ry (ĭn fûr'mạ rĭ), a hospital in a school or institution. (p. 106)

in ter cept′ (ĭn tẽr sĕpt′), to head off; to cut across the course of. (p. 89)

i′so lat ed (ī′sō lāt ĕd), set apart from others. (p. 265)

J

jag′ged (jăg′ĕd), with points sticking out. (p. 23)

Jol iet′, Lou′is (zhō lyĕ′, lōō′ĭ), a French-Canadian who explored the Mississippi. (p. 383)

junc′tion (jŭngk′shŭn), a joining. (p. 416)

ju′ni pers (jōō′nĭ pẽrz), an evergreen shrub with purple berries. (p. 185)

K

Kam chat′ka (kăm chȧt′kȧ), a peninsula in the northeastern part of Asia. (p. 350)

Kear′ney (kär′nĭ), a fort in the south-central part of Nebraska. (p. 414)

L

la goon′ (lȧ gōōn′), shallow water separated from a larger body of water. (p. 65)

laid waste (lād wāst), destroyed. (p. 51)

la ment′ (lȧ mĕnt′), mourn. (p. 380)

Lar′a mie (lăr′ȧ mĭ), a fort in Wyoming. (p. 419)

lard′er (lär′dẽr), a pantry. (p. 358)

laths (lȧthz), thin, narrow strips of wood. (p. 331)

lean′-to (lēn′tōō), a building held up by the building to which it is attached. (p. 259)

lo′cust (lō′kŭst), a tree with small rounded leaves and sweet-smelling flowers. (p. 74)

lum′ber ing (lŭm′bẽr ĭng), moving heavily. (p. 196)

lunged (lŭnjd), threw or hurled itself. (p. 8)

lu′pines (lū′pĭnz), blue flowers something like larkspur. (p. 368)

lust′y (lŭs′tĭ), strong and healthy. (p. 363)

M

ma che′te (mä chä′tā), a large, heavy knife with a broad blade. (p. 26)

Mag da le′na (mäg dä lä′nä), a river in Colombia. (p. 297)

main′sail (mān′sāl), the principal sail on the mainmast of a ship. (p. 276)

ma neu′ver ing (mȧ nōō′vẽr-ĭng), clever actions to produce conditions one wants. (p. 122)

---

dāte, ăm, fâre, ȧsk, ȧbout, fär, bē, mĕt, hẽre, makẽr, bīte, bĭt, hōpe, hŏt, lôrd, ūse, ŭp, bûrn, thin, then, pictŭre, fōōd, foŏt, out

marks'man ship (märks'măn-
shĭp), skill in shooting. (p.
407)

Mar quette', Jacques (màr kĕt',
zhàk), a French priest who explored the Mississippi. (p. 383)

mas'tiff (màs'tĭf), a large, strong
dog with drooping ears and
hanging lips. (p. 422)

me'sa (mā'så), a small, high
plateau with steep sides. (p.
368)

mes quite' (mĕs kēt'), a tree or
shrub that grows in the south-
western part of the United
States and in Mexico. (p. 73)

mess hall (mĕs hôl), the building in which a group of persons eat. (p. 338)

me'te or (mē'tē ẽr), a shooting
star. (p. 28)

mi gra'tion (mī grā'shŭn), a
moving from one region to another. (p. 56)

mis haps' (mĭs hăps'), unlucky
accidents. (p. 162)

Mi si o'nes (mē syō'nās), a territory in Argentina. (p. 306)

moat (mōt), a deep ditch around
a building to protect it; often
filled with water. (p. 374)

mu'ti nous (mū'tĭ nŭs), rebel-
lious. (p. 212)

myr'tle (mûr't'l), a shrub with
oval leaves and white or rosy
flowers. (p. 200)

432

N

New found land' (nū fŭnd-
lănd'), a large island east of
Canada. (p. 15)

nor'mal ly (nôr'măl lĭ), usually.
(p. 389)

O

out'law (out'lô), a person outside the protection of the law.
(p. 47)

out'skirts (out'skûrtz), the
outer parts. (p. 329)

o ver laid' (ō vẽr lād'), covered
over; coated. (p. 250)

o ver shad'ow ing (ō vẽr shăd'-
ō ĭng), casting a shadow. (p.
56)

P

pack'ing plant (păk'ĭng plànt),
a place where cattle, sheep,
and hogs are prepared as meat
for markets. (p. 151)

pal i sade' (păl ĭ sād'), a fence
of stakes set firmly in the
ground as a defense. (p. 374)

pal met'to (păl mĕt'ō), a palm
with fan-shaped leaves. (p.
197)

Pam'li co (păm'lĭ kō), a river in
the eastern part of North Carolina. (p. 195)

pam'pas (păm'påz), the vast
treeless plains of South America. (p. 52)

pan'nier (păn'yẽr), a large basket slung across the back of a horse, donkey, etc. (p. 290)

Pa ra na' (pä rä nä'), a long South American river. (p. 320)

par'ti cle (pär'tǐ k'l), a very small amount. (p. 169)

Pat a go'ni an (păt ạ gō'nǐ ăn), living in Patagonia, at the extreme south of South America. (p. 47)

pa'ti o (pä'tǐ ō), an inner courtyard, open to the sky. (p. 10)

ped'dle (pĕd''l), to carry from place to place and sell. (p. 14)

pen'du lum (pĕn' dū lŭm), a weight hung from a fixed point in such a way that it is free to swing to and fro. (p. 250)

pe'on (pē'ŏn), a laborer. (p. 25)

per plex'i ty (pẽr plĕk'sǐ tǐ), the state of not knowing what to do. (p. 76)

pe'sos (pā'sōz), Spanish coins. (p. 11)

pew'ter (pū'tẽr), made of tin mixed with lead. (p. 238)

phan'toms (făn'tŭmz), shadowy objects. (p. 365)

pheas'ant (fĕz'ănt), a food bird with a long tail and brilliant feathers. (p. 357)

pin'ions (pǐn'yŭnz), wings. (p. 32)

pip'pins (pǐp'ǐnz), apples. (p. 330)

plum'met (plŭm'ĕt), a weight fastened to a line. (p. 30)

pomp (pŏmp), great display; splendor. (p. 294)

pon'der ing (pŏn'dẽr ǐng), thinking over. (p. 412)

Pont gra vé' (pôn grä vä'), a French sea captain and fur trader. (p. 371)

pos'sum (pŏs'ŭm), a small animal that lives in trees. (p. 194)

pouch (pouch), a bag. (p. 392)

prec'i pic es (prĕs'ǐ pǐs ĕs), very steep places. (p. 295)

pre cip'i tous prē sǐp'ǐ tŭs), like a precipice; very steep. (p. 54)

Pri deau' (prē dō'), a French captain. (p. 384)

prime (prīm), first-class. (p. 266)

pro pos'al (prō pōz'ăl), suggestion. (p. 222)

pro test'ed (prō tĕst'ĕd), objected. (p. 18)

prune (prōōn), to cut out useless shoots or branches of a tree. (p. 182)

pu'mas (pū'mȧz), wildcats or mountain lions. (p. 51)

punt (pŭnt), a shallow, flat-bottomed boat with square ends. (p. 15)

---

dāte, ăm, fâre, ȧsk, ạbout, fär, bē, mĕt, hẹre, makẽr, bīte, bǐt, hōpe, hŏt, lôrd, ūse, ŭp, bûrn, thin, then, pictụre, fōōd, fŏŏt, out pu'ny-look ing (pū'nĭ lŏok ĭng), weak-looking. (p. 345)

Q

quad'ru ped (kwŏd'rŏo pĕd), a four-footed animal. (p. 299)

quar'ry (kwŏr'ĭ), a place where stone is dug or cut. (p. 35); in hunting, the game to be captured. (p. 201)

Que sa'da, Don Gon za'lo (kā-sä'thä, dôn gôn thä'lō), a Spanish explorer. (p. 297)

queue (kū), a braid. (p. 387)

quick'en ed (kwĭk'ĕnd), made lively, active. (p. 80)

quirt (kwûrt), a riding whip with a short handle and a lash of braided leather. (p. 403)

Qui'to (kē'tō), the capital of Ecuador in South America. (p. 24)

R

raf'ters (ràf'tērz), slanting beams of a roof. (p. 235)

raid'ing (rād'ĭng), making a surprise attack. (p. 299)

ra'tions (rā'shŭnz), daily allowance of food. (p. 419)

ra vine' (rạ vēn'), a long, deep, narrow valley. (p. 420)

raw'hide (rô'hīd), the untanned skin of cattle. (p. 262)

re as sured' (rē ă shŏord'), freed from fear. (p. 38)

re in force'ments (rē ĭn fōrs'-mĕntz), assistance. (p. 316)

re laxed' (rē lăkst'), loosened; became less stiff. (p. 93)

rel'ics (rĕl'ĭks), things left from the past. (p. 111)

re luc'tant (rē lŭk'tănt), unwilling. (p. 296)

re proved' (rē prōovd'), found fault with. (p. 331)

re sent'ful ly (rē zĕnt'fŏol ĭ), with a feeling of injury and anger. (p. 147)

re veil'le (rē văl'yĭ), a signal on a bugle or drum to waken soldiers or sailors. (p. 417)

rif'fles (rĭf'lz), shallow waters running swiftly over the bed of a river. (p. 363)

roo ta ba'ga (rŏo tạ bā'gạ), a vegetable like a turnip; usually spelled rutabaga. (p. 348)

ro ta'tion (rō tā'shŭn), planting a different crop from the one previously grown. (p. 151)

rou tine' (rŏo tēn'), ordinary; customary. (p. 139)

rush broom (rŭsh brŏom), a broom made of marsh plants called rushes. (p. 223)

S

Sag ue nay' (săg ē nā'), a river in Quebec. (p. 371)

sap'lings (săp'lĭngz), young trees. (p. 389)

sa'vor y (sā'vĕr ĭ), pleasing in taste. (p. 363)

scroll (skrōl), an ornament having the shape of a partly unrolled sheet of paper. (p. 248)

scrub growth (skrŭb grōth), a tangle of trees and shrubs. (p. 387)

sculp'tured (skŭlp'tūrd), modeled or carved. (p. 146)

scythe (sīth), a long, curved blade on a long handle, for cutting grass. (p. 170)

sea'far ing (sē'fâr ĭng), going to sea. (p. 276)

sea'soned (sē'z'nd), experienced. (p. 418)

sei gneurs' (sēn yûrz'), French word for lords. (p. 383)

self-as sured' (sĕlf ă shōord'), very much at ease. (p. 36)

se ra'pe (sĕ rä'pā), a blanket or shawl worn as an outer garment in Mexico. (p. 4)

shield (shēld), a metal disk attached to a strap. (p. 279)

shin'ers (shĭn'ĕrz), small, silvery fish. (p. 311)

shocked (shôkt), gathered into bundles set up on end together. (p. 145)

shrewd (shrōod), keen. (p. 329)

Sioux (sōo), belonging to the Sioux tribe of Indians. (p. 401)

sor'ghum mo las'ses (sôr'gŭm mō lăs'ĕz), molasses made from the juice of the sorghum plant. (p. 325)

spi'rals (spī'rălz), coils. (p. 56)

spot-cash (spŏt kăsh), money paid as soon as goods are obtained. (p. 350)

stam pede' (stăm pēd'), sudden and confused flight of a frightened herd. (p. 54)

star'board (stär'bōrd), the right side of a ship when one faces the forward part. (p. 20)

Stet'son hat (stĕt's'n hăt), a broad-brimmed hat. (p. 117)

stock (stŏk), the wooden part of a gun, which serves as a handle. (p. 206)

stub'ble (stŭb''l), growing short and rough. (p. 130)

sty'mied (stī'mĭd), blocked by another ball in the way. (p. 115)

sub merged' (sŭb mûrjd'), sunk under water. (p. 93)

su'macs (shōo'măks), shrubs or trees with divided leaves and crimson fruit. (p. 36)

sun'-dial (sŭn'dī ăl), an instrument for telling time by the position of a shadow. (p. 374)

su perb' (sū pûrb'), very fine. (p. 55)

---

dāte, ăm, fâre, ȧsk, ạbout, fär, bē, mĕt, hẽre, makẽr, bīte, bĭt, hōpe, hŏt, lôrd, ūse, ŭp, bûrn, thin, then, pictŭre, fōod, foŏt, out

su per nat'u ral (sū pēr năt'ū-răl), above or beyond what is natural. (p. 293)

sup ply' trains (sŭ plī' trānz), wagons carrying supplies. (p. 419)

sur vived' (sēr vīvd'), remained alive. (p. 298)

sus pend'ed (sŭs pĕnd'ĕd), hung down. (p. 27)

swale (swāl), meadow or marsh. (p. 368)

swarth'y (swôr'thĭ), having dark skin. (p. 212)

swirled (swûrld), moved with a twisting motion. (p. 17)

T

tack (tăk), sail in a zigzag course against the wind. (p. 78)

Ta dou sac' (tȧ dōō sȧk'), a village in Quebec near the mouth of the St. Lawrence. (p. 371)

tar pau'lin (tär pô'lĭn), a sheet of coarse, waterproofed cloth called canvas. (p. 118)

taut (tôt), drawn tightly. (p. 72)

taw'ny (tô'nĭ), brownish-yellow. (p. 7)

tem'po (tĕm'pō), rate. (p. 200)

tem'po rar y (tĕm'pō rĕr ĭ), lasting for a short time only. (p. 15)

ten-point (tĕn'point), having ten branches. (p. 367)

tense (tĕns), with mind and body ready for action. (p. 30)

ten'ta cles (tĕn'tȧ k'lz), long feelers able to grasp. (p. 20)

teth'er (tĕth'ēr), a rope or chain that keeps something fastened but allows it to move. (p. 142)

thir'ty-odd (thûr'tĭ ŏd), a few more than thirty. (p. 414)

till (tĭl), a small drawer for money. (p. 330)

till'er (tĭl'ēr), a bar or handle used to turn the rudder in steering a boat. (p. 125)

tim'o thy (tĭm'ō thĭ), coarse grass grown for hay. (p. 145)

tink'ered (tingk'ērd), repaired in an unskilled way. (p. 147)

tor til'la (tōr tē'yä), Mexican flat cake baked on a heated iron or stone. (p. 6)

trans ac'tions (trăns ăk'shŭnz), business dealings. (p. 330)

trap'pings (trăp'ĭngz), things worn. (p. 117)

trek (trĕk), journey. (p. 73)

trite (trīt), commonplace. (p. 139)

turn'stile (tûrn'stīl), a post with two crossed bars that turn, set in an entrance. (p. 331)

twinge (twĭnj), a sudden, sharp pain. (p. 361)

typ'i cal (tĭp'ĭ kăl), representative; like many others of the same kind. (p. 48)

U

un bro′ken (ŭn brō′kĕn), never tilled. (p. 231)

un cer′tain ty (ŭn sûr′tĭn tĭ), lack of facts. (p. 61)

un doubt′ed ly (ŭn dout′ĕd lĭ), without any doubt; surely. (p. 339)

un mis tak′able (ŭn mĭs tāk′ạ-b'l), that could not be taken for anything else. (p. 225)

un trod′den (ŭn trŏd′'n), not walked upon. (p. 367)

V

vats (vătz), tanks; large containers for liquids. (p. 60)

veg e ta′tion (vĕj ē tā′shŭn), growth of plants. (p. 292)

Ven e zue′la (vĕn ē zwē′lạ), a country in the northern part of South America. (p. 299)

ven′i son (vĕn′ĭ z'n), deer meat. (p. 240)

vol′ley (vŏl′ĭ), shower. (p. 65)

W

wal′low (wŏl′ō), a muddy place in which to roll. (p. 120)

wal′rus mus tache′ (wŏl′rŭs mŭs tàsh′), a mustache with long, drooping ends. (p. 324)

wan (wŏn), pale; tired-looking. (p. 212)

ward off (wôrd ŏf), to keep off. (p. 207)

war′i ly (wâr′ĭ lĭ), cautiously; carefully. (p. 74)

wa′ter fly (wô′tĕr flī), a fly that is found near water. (p. 371)

wa′ter logged (wô′tĕr lŏgd), stiff and heavy from being soaked with water. (p. 416)

weird (wērd), strange. (p. 335)

wel′kin (wĕl′kĭn), the sky; the dome of heaven. (p. 322)

whet′stone (hwĕt′stōn), a stone used for sharpening knives or tools. (p. 403)

whim′pered (hwĭm′pērd), cried with low, broken sounds. (p. 40)

Win′ches ter (wĭn′chĕs tēr), a sport rifle named after its maker. (p. 313)

wis te′ri a (wĭs tēr′ĭ ạ), a climbing shrub with large clusters of purple flowers. (p. 284)

wist′ful ly (wĭst′fŏŏl ĭ), with longing. (p. 36)

woes (wōz), troubles. (p. 298)

would′-be (wŏŏd′-bē), desiring to be. (p. 298)

wran′gler (răng′glēr), a man who rounds up horses on a range. (p. 119)

writh′ing (rīth′ing), twisting. (p. 21)

---

dāte, ăm, fâre, àsk, ạbout, fär, bē, mĕt, hẹre, makēr, bīte, bĭt, hōpe, hŏt, lôrd, ūse, ŭp, bûrn, thin, then, pictụre, fōōd, fŏŏt, out

ACKNOWLEDGMENTS

FOR permission to use copyrighted material, thanks are due the following publishers and authors:

D. Appleton-Century Company, publisher of *St. Nicholas,* for "Waukewa's Eagle," by James Buckham.

Dodd, Mead & Company, Inc., for "The Rays Defend the Ford," from *South American Jungle Tales,* by Horacio Quiroga.

E. P. Dutton & Co., Inc., for "Buffalo Bill," from *Heroes and Heroines,* by Eleanor and Herbert Farjeon; and "A Locomotive," from *Here and Now Story Book,* by Lucy Sprague Mitchell.

Farrar & Rinehart, Inc., for "P. T. Barnum," "Clara Barton," and "French Pioneers," from *A Book of Americans,* by Rosemary and Stephen Vincent Benét.

Frances Frost and the *American Girl,* for "Hike to the Hills."

Harcourt, Brace and Company, Inc., for "A Rootabaga Story" ("How They Broke Away to Go to the Rootabaga Country"), from *Rootabaga Stories,* by Carl Sandburg; and The Ryerson Press, for "The Rum Tum Tugger," from *Old Possum's Book of Practical Cats,* by T. S. Eliot.

Houghton Mifflin Company, for "The Deer-Star" and "A Song of Greatness," from *Children Sing in the Far West,* by Mary Austin; "The Buffalo Hunt," from *My Indian Boyhood,* by Chief Luther Standing Bear; and "A Letter from Quebec" ("Letter to Brother Guillaume"), from *Letters from Colonial Children,* by Eva March Tappan.

Little, Brown & Company, for "The Puritan Cat," from *Animal Pioneers,* by Catherine Cate Coblentz.

The Macmillan Company, for "Song of the Ship's Cat," from *Fair American,* by Elizabeth Coatsworth.

Portal and the author's daughter, Helen Finger, for "Ginger Follows the Trail" ("Fay's Bessie"), by Charles J. Finger.

Fleming H. Revell Company, for "Battle with a Giant Squid," from *The Adventures of Billy Topsail,* by Norman Duncan.

Story Parade, for "Meals for Mickey," by Alice Dalgliesh; "By Hook or Crook," by Nan Gilbert; "Corn-Belt Billy," by Mabel Leigh Hunt; and "Baby Rainstorm," by Glen Rounds.

Dorothy Brown Thompson and *Child Life,* for "The Boy Washington."

The John C. Winston Company, for "The Raft," from *Caroliny Trail,* by Alexander Key.

"Columbus," by Joaquin Miller, is reprinted by special permission of the author's daughter, Juanita J. Miller.

Thanks are also due those authors who have permitted slight editing of their material for further ease in reading.

438